BROMELIADS: The colorful house plants

BROMELIADS

THE COLORFUL HOUSE PLANTS

By JACK KRAMER

Drawings and Photographs by Andrew R. Addkison

D. VAN NOSTRAND COMPANY, INC.
Princeton, New Jersey
toronto • new york • london

D. VAN NOSTRAND COMPANY, INC.
120 Alexander St., Princeton, New Jersey (*Principal office*)
24 West 40 Street, New York 18, New York

D. VAN NOSTRAND COMPANY, LTD.
358, Kensington High Street, London, W.14, England

D. VAN NOSTRAND COMPANY (*Canada*), LTD.
25 Hollinger Road, Toronto 16, Canada

Published simultaneously in Canada by
D. VAN NOSTRAND COMPANY (Canada), LTD.

PRINTED IN THE UNITED STATES OF AMERICA

FOREWORD: Bromeliads Are for Everyone

As we enter the space age, it is interesting to observe that a most ancient family of plants, the *Bromeliaciae,* is becoming more and more popular—and rightly so. These air plants, as they are sometimes called, bloom indoors with a minimum of care, and the flowers and berries are so contemporary in color and form that they harmonize handsomely with the new concepts in architecture. Today many buildings, both public and private, are rather austere; their indoor garden areas require plants that are boldly decorative, their unadorned walls offering fine backgrounds for unusual plants in interesting containers. Bromeliads are living decorations of just the right kind, and apparently they have an intense desire to survive so that neglect does not often kill them.

Perhaps the first Bromeliad appeared as a house plant on a kitchen window sill when a cook cut off the top of a pineapple, a member of this group, and potted it. She was amazed to find that it grew rapidly and with little attention, and this is true of most Bromeliads. It was about eight years ago that I first saw Bromeliads in a Florida nursery. I had been growing Orchids at the windows of my apartment for some time and thereupon decided to try Bromeliads as well. They have proved just as undemanding and have richly rewarded me with their colorful foliage and brilliant exotic blooms. Visitors always want to know what they are, whether they are easy to raise, and I am glad to assure them that anyone can grow Bromeliads and almost anywhere.

Appreciation of these house and garden plants is increasing as they are better known through exhibits at flower shows and the efforts of The Bromeliad Society. This group welcomes members—address the Secretary, 1811 Edgecliff Drive, Los Angeles, 26—and issues an excellent *Bulletin* 6 times a year.

While little has been written in English on the *Bromeliaceae*, there are some fine French, German, and Spanish texts. I have read with great interest *Les Bromeliacées* by Leon Duval (1896), *Anzucht und Kultur der Bromeliaceen* by Walter Richter (1950), *Arquivos de Botanica de Estado De S. Paulo* by Lyman B. Smith (1943), and *Zimmerpflanzen von heute und morgen: Bromeliaceen* by Walter Richter (1962).

I find this flowering group extremely decorative and useful. There is always a Bromeliad in bloom in my plant room that I can move, pot and all, to accent a bare corner, or add drama to a dining room table or be a conversation piece on a coffee table. Used this way, Bromeliads demand little water, maybe once every five days, and foliage and flower color stay alive for many weeks, far outlasting any cut flowers.

The cultural notes given in this book are those I have adopted after much trial and error. Light is the most important factor in successful Bromeliad growing. Description of plants —foliage color, flower color—given here are under my own Midwest conditions. It should be expected that leaf and flower color may vary somewhat depending upon your growing conditions. Species names change frequently and those stated here are as accurate as I can obtain at present writing.

This book is not meant to be a technical discussion of *Bromeliaceae;* I leave that to botanists and taxonomists. Rather it is an account of the many Bromeliads I have successfully grown in my home under average conditions that are easily duplicated.

Chicago, Illinois   JACK KRAMER
January, 1965

CONTENTS

vii

ILLUSTRATIONS

PHOTOGRAPHS IN COLOR

1 BROMELIADS— PLANTS OF DOUBLE APPEAL

When I was a boy, my mother kept many pots of Sansevieria, Ivy, and Croton on the kitchen window sill. In the living room there were ferns and other green plants placed attractively for, knowingly or not, she used these as decoration. Later, Dracaena and Philodendron replaced them as they did in many homes in the United States. Variegated plants, too, such as Dieffenbachias and Caladiums, became favorites with multicolored leaves rather than the usual green foliage. Although many of these were flowering plants, in the home under adverse conditions, we had to be satisfied with the foliage alone. Now, a new inexpensive plant group is available to the home grower. One that offers both brilliant bloom and ornamental foliage—the Bromeliads.

Painted Feather, Queen's Tears, Rainbow Plant, Flaming Sword, Painted Fingernail, and Black Chantinii are but a few

1

of the glamorous names given to these superlative plants. Bromeliads are almost indestructible and are excellent for indoor decoration. Easy to grow, they come in different sizes, from miniatures to giants, with the greater number just right for indoors. The foliage is highly colorful, the flower scapes beautiful, and berries of many species last three to four months. Truly these are plants of double appeal, and with a dividend. Many can also be used outdoors where temperatures stay above freezing.

WHERE THEY GROW

Most Bromeliads come from South America with perhaps the greatest number of species from Brazil. Many are found in Mexico and Central America and a few in this country. In nature, they are mainly air plants or epiphytes growing high in tree tops in partial sunlight and using the branches as anchors; they are not parasites. There are also species that grow in the ground in shade as terrestrials and others that cling to rocks for survival. (A few grow in full sun in the desert.) Many genera grow under all three conditions. Some even endure life on other plants, such as cacti, or they may use telephone poles or wires as footholds.

Bromeliads are almost always found in areas of good air circulation. This is vital to their growth. Plants with thin leaves are most likely to be epiphytes, those with thick spiny leaves, terrestrials. However, it is possible for the same species to grow in a tree or on the ground. The intense will to survive is shown over and over again in this plant family. In the home, they adjust to our conditions and require less care than most other plants.

HOW THEY GROW

Some Bromeliads have a vase or bowl formation of leaves recurved to form a receptacle for food and holding half to a full cup of water. In the jungle, organic matter, insects, small frogs, and lizards drop into this reservoir. Some, no doubt, make their homes there; others, perhaps, die and decompose to furnish necessary nutrients for the plant. Bromeliads in cultivation are free of such pests or pets. In fact, their tough foliage is almost immune to insects.

In nature many Bromeliads do not have an extensive root system and as long as the vase holds water, they can live a long time without additional moisture. Attached to driftwood or grouped in dish gardens, they survive quite dry for many weeks. However, in pots with a porous soil mixture, plants develop larger root systems, further evidence of adaptability, and they do require water for roots as well as in the vases.

The circular rosette of thick leaves is most common among Aechmeas, while Nidulariums have flattened tops like a pressed fan. Vertical and tubular growth is prevalent among Billbergias. Large Tillandsias have narrow, tapered leaves in a graceful palm effect, and small species have tentacle or bristling growth. Vriesea foliage is rosette or tapered, the plants resembling handsome small bushes. Dyckias look like cactus and Cryptanthus species like starfish. Pitcairnias with spindly vertical foliage are not too attractive out of bloom, and many Quesnelias seem to fall between rosette and tubular growth patterns.

True Flowers

Flowers range from tiny, almost microscopic blossoms, as in some Hohenbergias to the large 2- to 3-inch flowers of *Tillandsia lindenii*. Although most species have small blooms that last only a few days, the floral bracts and berries often continue to be colorful for months. In many Bromeliads, the true flowers are hidden in the bracts, creating a charming effect like a miniature bouquet.

Flowers are usually red or pink, lavender or blue, although

white, yellow, green, and red are seen too. Few Bromeliads have odor. Two or three species of Tillandsias have a sweet fragrance and one elusive Aechmea species that blossomed for me last year was pleasantly scented. Other than these, I have not noticed fragrance.

FLOWER BRACTS AND FOLIAGE

With the flowers, Bromeliads have vivid bracts and spikes. These hold color for a long time in many species. Spikes have various forms from the branched candelabra growth of Aechmeas to the flamboyant pendent sprays of Billbergias or the low flower heads in the core of various Neoreglias. Some Guzmanias have a star-shaped inflorescence. Small Orthophytums look like tiny fountains of spiny leaves crowned red when in bloom.

Although the flower scapes are unusual and vivid, it is the unique foliage that is most attractive. Even without bloom, plants are effective because of the coloring and varied markings on the leaves. Many are in subtle shades of green-gray to yellow to red to brown. Then there are the beautiful plum-and-wine colored leaves of the Aechmeas. Some species have mottled foliage, others, horizontal or vertical stripes; some are spotted, others magnificently variegated. To me, the frosted green coloring of some Billbergias is the most handsome. You could grow Bromeliads just for their foliage since they are so different and offer such pleasing contrast to other house plants which are usually green.

2 | SELECTING AND BUYING YOUR FIRST PLANTS

As the world becomes smaller through jet travel with South America and Central America only hours away, more Bromeliads are being imported. Growers are hybridizing and stocking plants and every day new species are being discovered.

Bromeliads were first introduced to Europe in the middle of the nineteenth century when collectors of orchids included some species in the shipments. Their value as house plants was soon recognized and they became, and still are, popular as decorations. But it has only been recently that we have realized the tremendous potential of Bromeliads as house plants. They are tough to kill and will live even under untoward conditions. They are just right for those many places where other green plants will not survive.

5

For Seasonal Bloom

Bromeliads are not expensive. A mature specimen costs from two to seven dollars and plants multiply so freely that in a few years you recover the original cost. For example, I bought an *Aechmea filicaulis* for five dollars one year; later, I had six plants from it.

Like Orchids, there are Bromeliads that bloom in every season with the majority flowering in spring. Many species retain colorful bracts and berries for three to four months so you need only a few plants for year-round effect. However, exact flowering times cannot be guaranteed. Orchids are more or less predictable in this respect but Bromeliads are apt to be erratic, and some plants will not bloom at all. Others are fairly dependable. This information is given separately, with the description of each species in chapter 5.

Generally, I grow about forty plants at a time, ten for each season, and this gives me year-round color even if some do not bloom. Even without flowers, Bromeliads are handsome foliage plants. I have received only two plants that were a total loss and I was at fault both times. One plant I potted too tight and, since drainage was poor, the crown rotted. The other, put out on an open porch, was knocked down by wind and severely bruised.

Forcing Flowers

Some Bromeliads can be made to bloom out of season, but this should only be tried with mature and healthy specimens. To force a plant, apply a solution of $\frac{1}{4}$ ounce calcium carbide to 1 quart of water. Empty the plant cup and refill with this solution. Let it remain for twenty-four hours. Then, wash the cup out thoroughly and refill with plain water. Such treatment will bring Aechmeas, Billbergias, Guzmanias, Nidulariums, and Vrieseas into flower in four to nine weeks.

Buying Plants

The best buy is a medium-size plant about six months old. Ultimate size depends on species. Some are dwarf by nature, others, giants. Size will be indicated under each genus. I buy most of my Bromeliads from mail-order houses in the East and in southern Florida. If packed properly, the plants withstand rigors of transportation and three to five days en route do no harm. Unlike Orchids they can be shipped in winter except in periods of extreme cold. Foliage may lose color but otherwise plants arrive in good condition. Usually, they come bare root (without pots), and this is satisfactory.

New Arrivals

The first thing I do with new specimens is to wash them well with tepid water in the sink. I flush out the vase of each plant several times to make sure all living organisms are gone. I have yet to find any hidden insects but I go through this process anyway. Then I pot plants in osmunda or a terrestrial mix according to the species, and water well. Finally, plants are set aside in a shaded place. *This is important.* Sudden exposure to sun after the darkness of a shipping box is harmful. In a few days, I move the new Bromeliads to a lighter position and in another few days, I place them according to their light requirements at windows.

First Selection

It is difficult to say which Bromeliads to try first. It depends on the colors you like or perhaps the structure of inflorescence and whether you are interested in the decorative value of handsome foliage. If you are fond of Caladiums and Crotons, Bromeliads will steal your heart. Here are two excellent groups, one for striking color, one for handsome foliage.

For Flowers and Bracts	For Foliage
Aechmea fasciata	*Aechmea chantinii*
A. fulgens var. *discolor*	*Cryptanthus* species
Billbergia pyramidalis var.	*Guzmania vittata*
concolor	*Neoreglia carolinae tricolor*
Guzmania lingulata	*Vriesea hieroglyphica*
Nidularium regelioides	

These flowering types are all dependable and adjust readily to home conditions. They are quite sure to bloom. The foliage types also bear flowers but for me their remarkable leaf coloring has just as much appeal as the blooms. Your choice is really a matter of taste, and also of how much you care to spend.

3 GROWING BROMELIADS IN YOUR HOME

In nature, Bromeliads decorate the landscape, the tree tops and forest floors where they enjoy natural air currents, rainfall, humidity, and seasonal temperatures. Try as we may, we cannot duplicate these conditions in the home. Therefore the plants must adjust to our environment; Bromeliads do this faster and better than any other plant group I know. I have seldom lost even a leaf in process of adjustment.

WHERE TO PLACE YOUR PLANTS

Bromeliads will thrive at windows of every exposure. When they bloom, you can move them about for table decoration or corner accents. I have had a *Neoreglia carolinae* in my living room that was colorful for three months. The way you want to use your plants will largely determine

9

where you place them. Many of my Bromeliads are grown with my Orchids. Others are on kitchen and bedroom window sills in 3-foot plastic boxes. I set the pots on bricks placed lengthwise in the box. This way, it is easy to water, drain-off is absorbed by the bricks and remaining water creates humidity.

Plastic trays, available in various sizes are a great convenience, and sheet-metal houses make galvanized metal trays that can also be fitted to window sill space. Use a 2-inch deep pan with rolled edges to avoid sharpness. Fill the box to within $\frac{1}{2}$ inch of the top with crushed stone and set pots on this. Small Bromeliads are especially effective this way. Water the same way as with the plastic boxes.

With larger specimens, a handsome arrangement can be made in trays on the floor under windows. Use a 4-inch deep metal tray and fill to within $\frac{1}{2}$ inch of the top with crushed stone. Arrange pots on this. A border of bricks can be used to hide the edge of the tray. The metal boxes prevent water marks on window sills or floors. Or try radiator pans that are still leakproof.

Bromeliads do not resent being moved about where temperatures and humidity vary. Plants readily adjust. If you wish, put each pot in standard clay or rubberized saucer and move plants from room to room to suit your decorative needs. I should mention, however, that cats and dogs are attracted to the succulence of most Bromeliad foliage and delight in chewing at them so keep your plants away from pets.

If your windows are obscured by tall buildings and additional light is needed, fluorescent lighting is the answer. You can now buy ready-made stands or trays with tubes to accommodate ten to twenty plants and provide adequate "sunshine" for their needs. Set plants with tops of leaves 12 to 15 inches from the tubes. Sun-loving species like *Ananas comosus* and *Hechtia rosea* need about sixteen hours, partial-shade varieties about thirteen hours. An automatic timer can be used to control on-and-off periods. These are only general rules. As yet, little has been done with Bromeliads under artificial light so you must depend for guidance on your own observation. I have found that fluorescent light encourages leaf growth but has little effect on bloom.

TEMPERATURE

Bromeliads thrive in average house temperatures. During the day, 70 to 85 degrees F. is fine; at night, in winter, 52 to 65 degrees suits most species. In summer, it will be warmer but not much can be done about this for plants or humans. In fall and winter, I use no supplementary heating on the sunporch and from midnight to 6 A.M., the temperature drops down into the 50's, as in nature. These cool nights keep Bromeliads healthy.

I haven't tried it but I suspect that many Bromeliads will live on an unheated sunporch provided the temperature doesn't go below freezing. This should certainly be true of species from the mountains of Peru, Colombia, and Ecuador where nights are very cold. These include some Ronnbergias and Greigias and a few Streptocalyx species.

WATERING AND FERTILIZING

The vase form of the Bromeliad suggests that the cup be kept filled with water. In this regard, I follow nature through spring, summer, and fall, but in winter, I let my plants dry out somewhat. It seems doubtful that the compost in which they grow should be kept moist throughout the year. In any season, I find that some drying between waterings is beneficial. In summer and in fall, I water plants about every third day. In winter and spring, I water every fourth or fifth day, depending upon whether the sun is bright or it is cloudy or rainy. These are my general rules.

Occasionally, a plant just looks dry. The appearance of the foliage, the whole attitude suggests a need for moisture so I immerse the pot up to the rim in water for about twenty minutes to give roots a really good soaking. It is difficult to say how much water to give a plant. Temperature, humidity, air circulation, and sun are all factors. It would be wonderful to have a proper balance for then the problem of watering would be easy. As it is, we must use common sense and consider all the conditions under which a Bromeliad grows.

As with most indoor plants, a shower in the sink once every two weeks is wise procedure. It leaches out built-up acids in the soil and is generally beneficial. In summer, I set many Bromeliads outside on a porch where they can get rain. It is amazing what a few weeks of outdoor life will do. Rain water and air refresh plants noticeably.

Doubtless in nature, leaves and debris decompose in the vases of these air plants, providing nutrients essential to growth. Under cultivation, they require a weak compensating fertilizer. I use a 10-5-5 solution once every two weeks in spring and summer, but not through the rest of the year.

Humidity

I have grown Bromeliads in a bedroom where humidity averages 30 to 50 per cent, sometimes less. I also have some on the sunporch where the humidity is 50 to 70 per cent, sometimes higher. The two groups do equally well so I believe that humidity is a minor factor in culture. However, I would not suggest growing Bromeliads (or any other green plants) where humidity goes below 30 per cent without misting the foliage a few times a day in spring and summer. Or use a space humidifier.

Air Circulation

In nature, Bromeliads are rarely found in ravines, but mostly on the edge of rocks or cliffs, high in trees, or in the mountains where air is cool and moist. In other words, they grow where there is free movement of air. *This is vital* to their health and the most important aspect of home culture. Bromeliads will not thrive in a stuffy atmosphere.

In summer, and whenever weather permits in other seasons, I keep windows near the plants open even through the night. In inclement weather, when windows must be closed, I run a small fan near the plants to create a gentle flow of air. This also discourages disease and insects. However, as with all plants, direct drafts should be avoided.

Since Bromeliad roots benefit from air as much as the leaves, I suggest Orchid pots with slotted sides or any other container that has side openings. It is also beneficial to place pots so air can circulate around them. You might try hanging pots with wires from curtain rods or use wire baskets now available at most florists. Remember that the more air Bromeliads get, the better they grow.

Light

Good light is essential for the growth of Bromeliads as it is for all plants. Varying degrees of light might be classified as: full sun, partial sunlight, diffused light, and semishade. In the Bromeliad plant group there are species for all conditions. Of course, total shade is to be avoided. It is wise to select your plants according to window space and available natural light. Ananas and Bromelia need full sun, most Aechmeas and Billbergias will want partial sunlight; Tillandsia and Neoreglia species do well in diffused light, and some Guzmanias and Vrieseas thrive at a north window. Light requirements will be discussed with each plant group.

Time of year must be considered, too. Between April 1st. and September 1st. in our northern latitude a south or east window must be shaded or plants develop leaf burn. In fall and winter, with shorter days and sunlight not so intense, shading is unnecessary. In temperate climates, shading might

be needed all year. Afternoon sun through all seasons is beneficial for a great number of Bromeliads so my plants are
placed mostly at west windows. It is interesting to see how
foliage changes color with the degree of light. In this respect,
Bromeliads are like Crotons. In good light, Crotons have stunning red foliage; in shade, they stay green.

If a plant does not respond at one exposure, move it around
until you find a spot where it grows better. This procedure
works for me.

POTTING MIXTURES AND POTS

Pot epiphytic and rock-growing Bromeliads in osmunda.
Because this material is not a solid mass, it dries quickly and
offers excellent drainage which is vital to growth. Orchid fir
bark can also be used for these species. Terrestrial plants need
a mixture of leafmold, manure, and sand with some crushed
rock. Or, if you care to, experiment with a compost of your
own, but make sure of good drainage and aeration of roots.

Since the leaves of Bromeliads are hard and durable, the
weakest part of the plant is the core. If the vase holds water
too long, and the water does not drain off naturally in the
compost, a plant is apt to rot at this vulnerable point. Water
is applied vertically to all plants but especially to Bromeliads
with their tubular or urn-shaped growth that holds water and
slowly releases it to the plant as needed. If plants are potted
too tight, water cannot drain off and rot develops at the base.

Small containers are best for most species, further protec-
tion against a stagnant compost since small pots dry out faster
than large ones. The standard orchid clay pot in the 4- or
5-inch size is good, even for larger specimens. I have a *Billbergia zebrina* that is almost 4 feet high in a 4-inch pot. This
is top heavy, especially when the tube is filled with water,
so I devised a method of propping the plant. I use slender
bamboo stakes pushed deep into the compost at the edge of

the pot. Then I loop string around the upper part of the plant and tie it to the stakes as an anchor. I do not like plastic pots, for they are not heavy enough to support large Bromeliads. Hanging orchid baskets with openings between the slats are fine for pendent species like *Aechmea filicaulis* and some of the Billbergias. In baskets, plant in osmunda only.

The potting of Bromeliads is a relatively simple business. Just proceed as you do with most house plants using cleaned pots and pot shards. I soak the osmunda overnight and fill pots one-third full with small stones or pot shards (just a few pieces). I work the osmunda to the center of the pot firming it with my thumbs or a blunt stick. Avoid setting the base of the plant so deep that there is danger of crushing the lower part of the leaf cup. Some Bromeliads do not have much root system, and these are difficult to handle. They can be propped up with stakes, as suggested above, until roots develop. Many Bromeliads can be grown on pieces of tree fern or orchid slabs and will respond beautifully.

As plants are potted, trim off excess osmunda with a scissors and label each specimen.

PEST AND DISEASE

Bromeliads are amazingly free of trouble. They never seem to get mealy bugs or red spider, common to so many house plants. With Bromeliads, it is safe to say they will not be bothered by insects of any kind. The leaves are just too tough.

The Aechmea scale is a possible enemy of these air plants, but I have found it only once. The small, black, hard-shelled insects with sucking appendages attach themselves to the leaves, usually the undersides. About the size of a pinhead, they have a covering that is impervious to most insecticides. However, you can scrape off scale with the dull edge of a knife; try not to bruise the foliage as you work. Soap and water and a stiff brush may get rid of them too if the attack is not advanced. Bromeliads react poorly to insecticides so it is better to avoid even the standard commercial products if you can. However, if absolutely necessary, use a very mild solution of malathion.

Fungus diseases are no problem if plants are given a good circulation of air. Avoid crowding Bromeliads. For good form and good health, allow each one plenty of space. Remember these are air plants.

PROPAGATION

Bromeliads produce more offshoots or suckers than most plants; they are almost too free in this respect, and it is not uncommon for one mother plant to have half a dozen offspring. Sometimes, this is a problem; it's difficult to throw them away but there does come a time when there is no more space. Since Bromeliads bloom but once, nature thus compensates with this abundance of offshoots.

The growth habit of offshoots differs among the genera. *Aechmea* send shoots to the side and the parent plant lives on for some months. *Neoreglia* develop new growth close to the mother plant. The suckers of *Vriesea* start in the cup close to the flower stem. Eventually, they choke off the parent. *Cryptanthus* species make offshoots on top of the rosette in leaf axils. When these are large enough, they can be pinched off the mature plant. Most Bromeliads produce offshoots after flowering, but some species start the new growth both before and at blooming time. Tubular Billbergias have fewer suckers than most Bromeliads.

In the genera *Aechmea*, *Nidularium*, and *Quesnelia*, suckers are produced on hard stems or stolons that are easily seen. In *Nidularium*, the stolon is shorter. It is a matter of personal judgment when to remove the new growth. Some growers claim the more offshoots you remove, the more you will have. I wait until there are at least three good-sized leaves and the stem or stolon is woody. Then I sever the offshoots with a sterile knife. A sharp clean cut is best, and I dust exposed new growth with charcoal. Pot immediately in 2- or 3-inch containers with the potting mix suggested for each genus in the specific discussions.

With small plants, keep humidity around 60 per cent and temperature as high as possible. About 80 degrees F. is best and never below 60 degrees at night.

As a rule, offshoots flower in a year or two. *Billbergia* and *Cryptanthus* may bloom the next year. *Aechmea, Neoreglia,* and *Vriesea* take one to two years. Many also produce seeds, but it is hardly practical to grow Bromeliads from seed at home.

4 ENJOYING BROMELIADS— INDOORS AND OUT

As indoor plants, Bromeliads have no equal. They are striking decorations at low cost compared to other house plants in effective sizes, and they are easily obtained, while large Dracaenas and Potocarpus are often difficult to find.

Bromeliads make fine vertical accents against plain walls. Billbergias, with their tall tubular growth look handsome on low tables. Aechmeas and Guzmanias offer attractive whirls of color; Vrieseas and large Tillandsias are graceful and palm-like. The flat fans of Neoreglias and Nidulariums are fine for a dim corner or for a coffee table where color is appreciated. Cryptanthus species look well almost anywhere; a row of these small plants at a kitchen window is always pleasing. Rooms in contemporary style with low tables and chests are enhanced by well-placed Bromeliads for both plant and flower form have a modern air.

In lobbies and the foyers of motels, hotels, and apartment buildings, indoor plantings are now almost essential. Certainly artificial specimens leave much to be desired, especially when they get dusty. For these big areas, Bromeliads are indeed the answer, even when they are grown at a northern exposure.

If you have an indoor garden, do try some of these air plants among your green plants. They will brighten them up delightfully. A striped *Aechmea chantinii* or a plum-colored *Aechmea fulgens discolor* offers contrast and drama. If you have planter boxes, you will find that Bromeliads do better in them than almost any other plants.

Many Bromeliads—*Aechmea angustifolia,* for instance— have brilliant fruit that lasts two to three months. Then the color fades and the berries shrivel but remain. A unique effect can be achieved by spraying with gold or silver paint. The metallic covering magnifies the depressions and markings of the dried berries, and they shine brilliantly as artificial light strikes the many facets in a decoration that lasts for months. This is something unusual for a table in an entrance hall or in the dining room. The flower scape with berries and bracts can also be cut off and placed in an opaque vase (without water) to make an attractive study in line and texture against a dark wall.

How to Make a Bromeliad Tree Garden

Select a shallow round or rectangular container 3- to 4-inches deep so that it can support a branch about 24 inches tall. The idea is to make a miniature of what might be seen in nature where dead trees devoid of foliage look handsome with Bromeliads and Orchids growing on them.

Since dead trees are often gnarled, look for a branch or

section of driftwood for your Bromeliad tree that also has interesting form. A piece with a high right or left curve is fine. Anchor the wood in a nest of crumpled florist wire. Then fill the dish with white pea gravel and top with sphagnum. Or you can set the branch in plaster of Paris (available at hardware stores) with a surface covering of stones.

When I make a tree garden, I attach plants to the branch before setting it permanently in the container, but you can trim the tree after setting the branch if you wish. Either way, the Bromeliads must be firmly affixed. It works well to cover roots with sphagnum moss and wire the clumps around the branch. Use plastic covered wire from a floral-supply house. *Do not use galvanized wire;* this causes leaf burn if it touches the foliage.

For a pleasing composition, put larger plants at the base and fasten smaller plants up the tree. The striped-leaf species, like *Aechmea chantinii* and *Vriesea hieroglyphica*, are effective for the bottom of the driftwood. Small Tillandsias look well on the tree itself, and also many of the Vrieseas.

Space plants to follow the curve of the branch. You might select varieties from only one genus; many species of Cryptanthus could be grouped at the base with smaller plants of the same family running up the tree. Watering of such an arrangement is simple; just take the whole thing to the kitchen sink and spray it there, or leave it in place and water with a basting syringe.

MINIATURE ROCK GARDENS AND TERRARIUMS

Bromeliads make attractive indoor rock gardens. They are one plant group that will survive this situation where other plants usually succumb after a short time. A 2- by 3-inch deep aluminum baking dish or a metal box filled with gravel makes a good container. On this, put interesting small rocks or stones. Then arrange pots of Bromeliads on the gravel with the rocks as background. Small plants of *Cryptanthus* and *Vriesea* are handsome in these compositions.

The same idea can be used to make a terrarium. Spread 2 inches of a gravel-and-sand mixture over the bottom of a 5-gallon aquarium. Set in small stones and interesting pieces of branch and set potted Bromeliads (or plants without pots with roots wrapped in sphagnum) to create a pleasing design. I arrange the greenery from the back corners of the tank to front center, larger species in the rear and smaller subjects forward.

I select plants of *Cryptanthus* because I know they will thrive there. Then the highly colored foliage with wavy bands suggests starfish and in the changing light and under the distortion of glass, the terrarium looks like an undersea garden. Tiny ferns or other dwarf plants can be added. Set the terrarium away from the sun, preferably at a north exposure close to the window and cover with a pane of glass cut 2 inches shorter in the width than the top of the terrarium. This will allow air to circulate inside and plants remain healthy.

I do not really water plants in my terrarium. Instead, about twice a week I mist them with tepid water, using a window cleaning spray bottle.

In Patio and Courts

Patios and outdoor living areas are now an aspect of our way of life even where summers are short. For these areas, Bromeliads are ideal. In climates where it is safe to have plants outside only from June to September, leave the Bromeliads in pots and, when weather permits, arrange them outdoors in decorative compositions. A rock or large tree makes an effective background.

Glassed-in atriums or courts that stay above freezing are also natural locations for cold-tolerant Bromeliads. On severe nights, small space heaters can be turned on. Where it would be costly to fill these open areas with large green plants, it is inexpensive to use Bromeliads, which readily survive the shift from outdoors to in and can be utilized for decoration all year.

Most species have tough foliage that withstands heavy rains better than that of many plants. Just three or four large tubs of air plants can transform a bare area into a handsome garden.

In Gardens

In a garden in a temperate climate, a wide selection of species can be planted directly into soil of average fertility. Select plants to accent the contour of a hill or embankment, or substitute Bromeliads for a wire fence; many are heavily spined and make impenetrable boundaries.

Most large Bromeliads have very tall flower spikes that rise high above the plants and are spectacular. With many outdoor plants, flowers are lost in foliage. At night, Bromeliads in the garden are astonishingly beautiful when spotlighting illuminates their structural forms and emphasizes the colorful shading of the leaves.

Outdoors, in summer, it is best to water plants daily unless there is heavy rain. However, Bromeliads being air plants can stand long dry periods and will not suffer unduly if you must be away for a week or so. Under similar circumstances, ferns, palms, and begonias would probably die.

When you select Bromeliads for the garden, keep in mind the individual light requirements as they are indicated in the descriptions that follow. Bare places under large open-leaved trees suit many Bromeliads since enough sunshine for their needs filters through the leaves.

BROMELIADS ON TREES

Like Orchids, Bromeliads can be attached to tree trunks or low branches. Small Tillandsias are effective grown in this way and do better than if left in pots. If you use trees directly as hosts, be sure plants are tightly affixed. Wrap roots in sphagnum and osmunda and then wire each ball firmly to the tree.

SUMMERING PLANTS OUTDOORS

Lacking a patio, I summer many of my air plants on an open back porch where they are placed against a brick wall. I set them out late in May and take them in as soon as it starts to turn cool, that is, 54 degrees at night in my locale; this is usually in early October. I also enjoy several potted Bromeliads grouped in a garden patch underneath tall bushes, and they do well there.

For outdoor plantings, Bromeliads are adaptable, colorful, and inexpensive and should certainly be used more. Here is a list of species particularly suited to the open garden. These will endure 32 degrees at night, although 40 to 50 degrees is safer.

Cold-Tolerant Bromeliads

A. calyculata	*Neoreglia* species
Aechmea x maginali	*Nidularium* species
A. weilbachii	*Portea petropolitana* var.
Billbergia Fantasia	*extensa*
B. nutans	*Tillandsia ionantha*
Dyckia fosteriana	*T. lindenii*
D. frigida	

5 | 150 COLORFUL BROMELIADS

ACANTHOSTACHYS

Acanthostachys from Argentina, Paraguay, and Brazil is a genus with but one species: *A. strobilacea*. It is an unusual plant; most decorative and best grown in a hanging basket. The fruit resembles small orange-colored pineapples and holds color for three to four months.

With pendent growth, the plant has a sculptured form that is effective when set off by a white wall. My plant is in a 3-inch pot suspended with a 12-inch orchid pot hanger. It is centered on the outside moulding of a window where vertical accent is needed. It grows well here with little care.

A. strobilacea has pendent whiplike leaves to 36 inches; they are reddish brown. The small orange pineapple is surrounded by stiff bracts.

Grow this plant in a 2- or 3-inch pot with a sandy terres-

1

ACANTHOSTACHYS STROBILACEA

trial mix. Water heavily during growth in spring and summer but keep it only moderately moist the rest of the year. This species needs some sun but also succeeds at a north window. If you use this Bromeliad for a hanging basket, group several plants together and grow it into a specimen. Do not bother the offshoots. A most useful species for home decoration.

AECHMEA

Aechmea is a genus of mainly epiphytic Bromeliads distributed from Mexico to Argentina. They are handsome even out of flower. The leaf pattern is in the form of a tubular open vase or of a rosette, and the flower spike develops in the center, rising well above the foliage. Flowers are attractive, but it is the fruit of many species, the vivid berries, that makes this genus outstanding because the color lasts for months. Leaves are leathery or soft, banded or of one color, with tiny marginal spines.

The inflorescence takes various forms but usually is erect and somewhat branched. Some species have handsome tufted flower crowns while others are cylindrical or cone-shaped. I grow about twenty different Aechmeas. They are readily available, easy to care for, and the majority are dependable about blooming.

A. angustifolia, grows to about 24 inches and has narrow leathery leaves. White berries appear after the spring blossoming. In a few weeks they turn brilliant blue and remain on the plant for two months.

A. calyculata is of medium size with dark green leaves. The compact flower head brings a butter-yellow color to the window sill all through the winter. This one will do best with

2

AECHMEA CALYCULATA

good light and some coolness, about 55 degrees F. at night, in winter.

A. caudata var. *variegata* would be a good investment for its handsome foliage even if it never flowered. The leaves are yellow-white and green-striped. The flower head, yellow-orange, erect, and striking, usually appears in winter. This is one of the few difficult Aechmeas but a healthy specimen is worth the effort.

A. chantinii, the Queen of the Aechmeas, is indeed handsome. Leaves are olive-green with silver bands. The large flower head is upright, a vivid red and yellow. Of medium-size, this regal plant gives weeks of pleasure when it blooms in spring.

A. distichantha var. *schlumbergeri* grows to 36 inches or more with stiff heavily spined leaves. The violet flowers and bright rose bracts make it effective outdoors. Needs little care and is not particular about temperature.

A. fasciata, with 24-inch leaves, sometimes called the urn plant, is a window gardener's delight. It produces a large pink inflorescence with hundreds of tiny blue flowers in summer. Fine for the beginner, sure to bloom.

A. filicaulis has satiny green leaves and dancing white flowers and red bracts on a thin pendent spike that comes alive in the slightest breeze. This unusual and decorative Aechmea is well suited to basket culture.

A. Foster's Favorite is reliable with wine-red foliage and dark blue winter flowers followed by red berries. A small inexpensive air plant readily accommodated at a window.

A. fulgens var. *discolor* is a favorite of mine, with maroon-shaded green leaves. In spring, it produces dark purple flowers followed by rose-colored berries that last for three months. It is well suited to a limited space and will survive considerable neglect.

A. luddemanniana grows to 40 inches with arching green

3

AECHMEA LUDDEMANNIANA

leaves. The panicle is crowded with lavender flowers maturing into a dense head of blue and white berries that eventually turn purple and last for months. *A real house plant.*

A. Maginali (*A. miniata discolor* × *A. fulgens discolor*) is a lovely hybrid with plum-colored leaves about 20 inches long and blue flowers in June or July. The orange-brown berries last till autumn. Dependable and highly recommended.

A. mertensii is delightful, neat and small with a cone-shaped inflorescence covered with red-to-yellow flowers. Bright orange bracts compliment the flower crown and the apple-green foliage. When mature, blue berries appear and hold color from November to April.

A. mexicana grows to 3 feet with pale green leaves spotted darker green. In winter or spring, a large cylindrical head of crimson flowers is followed by white berries.

A. nudicaulis var. *aureo-rosea*, a medium-size plant with silver-green spiny leaves and red-and-yellow flowers, bears brilliant pink berries. Usually this blossoms in summer and needs more sun than most Aechmeas.

A. orlandiana with an orange spike of white-and-yellow flowers in winter has pale green leaves with purple-brown bands. Give this one more heat than others in the genus. Leaf color varies considerably with light exposure. Although this has been difficult to get to bloom under my conditions, it is a worthwhile addition to a Bromeliad collection.

A. ornata, an attractive foliage plant with a cluster of thinly-tapered leaves, puts forth a pale rose-colored pyramidal flower crown at unpredictable times. Needs full sun.

A. penduliflora, of medium size, is spindly with tapered leaves and blue-and-white berries following the spring flowers.

A. pineliana var. minuta, a dwarf with a delightful rosette of

AECHMEA RACINAE

black, spiny green-copper leaves and straight red bracts of yellow bristling petals, is an unusual Bromeliad.

A. pubescens with leaves to 30 inches is decorative in bloom and afterwards in April when the white berries turn blue. Requires more light than other Aechmeas.

A. racinae is small with light green leaves and yellow-and-black flowers on a pendent spike. The orange-red berries appear appropriately at Christmas time and last until April. Try this one in a hanging basket and grow it in light shade.

A. ramosa, of medium size, has waxy green leaves and a large branched yellow flower head with rose-colored bracts followed by greenish berries. A handsome Aechmea that holds color for many months.

A. recurvata var. *ortgiesii* is also small with thorny cactus-like foliage and a low pink flower head. Grow it on the dry side and in sun.

A. weilbachii var. *weilbachii* grows to about 30 inches with green leaves and an almost pendent branching red-and-lavender inflorescence in late fall. Very decorative and a good grower.

My Aechmeas are grown in osmunda with charcoal chunks spread over the bottom of the pot. A terrestrial mix can also be used. In potting, assure good drainage and aeration. Small pots, 3-4- or 5-inch, are adequate even for the larger plants.

Almost any light exposure suits this genus, although strong summer sun should be avoided. My plants are at a west window all year and get two to three hours of afternoon sunlight. I keep them evenly moist in spring and summer, the vases filled with water. In autumn and winter, I allow a drying-out between waterings, and only in winter do I reduce the amount of water in the cup.

Temperature for Aechmeas should not go below 54 degrees F. at night in winter, and 58 degrees is better, although a few cold nights will not harm the plants. Moderate humidity is necessary during the day, say 30 to 60 per cent, and about 40 per cent at night. Aechmeas are less temperamental about air circulation than most Bromeliads.

Propagation is generally by offshoots produced at the base of the plant; these stolons are easily removed with a knife when they are one-third the size of the mother plant. Aechmea scale sometimes attacks so inspect plants regularly. If scale is present, get rid of it with a stiff brush dipped in a mild soap-and-water solution.

ANANAS

Ananas is a genus of mainly large plants found in Brazil with a few from Venezuela and Paraguay. The pineapple is a member of this family. The leaves are spiny and handsomely variegated. Although the species are difficult to bring into bloom, the striking red inflorescence is worth the effort.

There are four species readily available; I have grown *A. bracteatus*, *A. comosus*, and *A. nanus*. The sharp-edged leaves are annoying when handling these plants, but otherwise I find them excellent house plants.

A. bracteatus has 40-inch dark green leaves that turn handsome red in sunlight. A good Bromeliad if you have the space.

A. comosus is the commercial pineapple plant. The stiff leaves are variegated and the purple flowers are produced at the top of an erect stalk.

A. nanus is a dwarf species with satiny green leaves 10 to 14 inches long; it is available at florist shops and somewhat resembles *A. comosus*. The small pineapple is decorative on its stiff stalk.

5

ANANAS COMOSUS

Ananas require a terrestrial compost, and larger species can well be grown in big tubs or pots where they develop into handsome specimens for gardens and patios where temperatures do not drop below 50 degrees F. at night, in winter.

Although they tolerate shade, these Bromeliads do better in direct sun which produces brighter leaf color. Water liberally and often except in the cold months but allow for a drying-out between waterings. Average home temperatures are suitable, but humidity of 40 to 50 per cent is necessary. Decorative for either the indoor or outdoor garden.

ARAEOCOCCUS

Araeococcus is a genus of terrestrial and epiphytic Bromeliads from Costa Rica, Trinidad, Tobago, Venezuela, and northern Brazil. Of the four species known, two are available and decorative. Ribbon leaves are produced from a bulbous base; the slender scape is composed of pale red flowers. Both species are easily grown at a window.

A. flagellifolius is small with narrow reddish foliage, pink flowers, and blue-black berries on a short scape. Of unusual appearance.

A. pectinatus, another small grower, has reddish bronze leaves and a red inflorescence.

My plants are at a west window where they are watered moderately all year. They are in a terrestrial mix but osmunda can also be used; 2- or 3-inch pots are best. Although not very showy, Araeococcus species have a decorative charm and, since they take up little space, I recommend them for the window garden.

ARAEOCOCCUS FLAGELLIFOLIUS

BILLBERGIA

Billbergia is a large genus mainly from eastern Brazil with a few species from Mexico and South America. This is a wonderfully versatile group with many shapes, colors, and sizes; above all, an easy-to-grow genus for the home. They thrive under varied conditions.

Most species are tall and tubular like *B. horrida* and *B. zebrina;* others, like *B. pyramidalis* make sprawling rosettes similar to the Aechmeas and some are small funnel-shaped plants like *B. saundersii* and *B. euphemiae*. Flowers vary in their color combinations, the most daring perhaps being the rose, green, and blue of *B. nutans.*

The genus is characterized by trailing or pendent scapes with bright rose bracts, although a few species have an erect inflorescence. The flower head can be a dense crown, or a group of widely-set flowers. Plants are dramatic when in bloom but flowers do not last long. In most species, foliage color is varied and showy when grown in good light.

Among Billbergias are species that bloom in each season; by careful selection you can have year-round color at the window. This genus is so interesting and varied, you can have a Bromeliad collection of Billbergias alone. Many species are available and most are inexpensive; there are also many fine hybrids. I grow more than a dozen of this genus and recommend them to the beginner or advanced hobbyist.

B. amoena var. *amoena* of medium tubular size has green leaves and rose-colored bracts. Flowers are green with blue edges.

B. amoena var. *viridis,* a handsome medium-size tubular

BILLBERGIA EUPHEMIAE

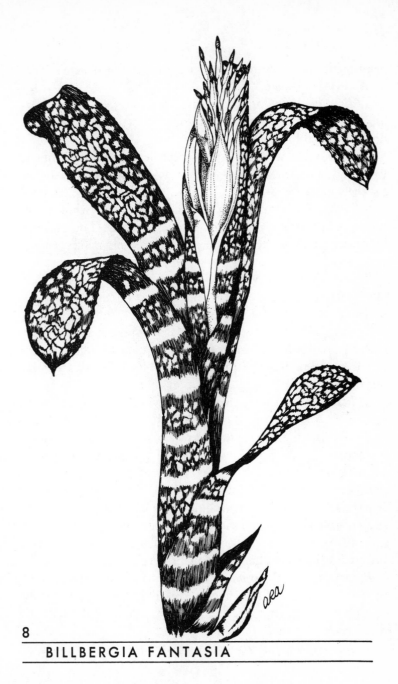

BILLBERGIA FANTASIA

plant with ivory-spotted green leaves and green petals blossoms in April for me.

B. distachia, small and bulbular, has green leaves with purple coloring, the cascading scape has pink bracts and green flowers tipped blue.

B. euphemiae, with stiff gray-green leaves and pink bracts with dark blue petals blooms in any season. Not as showy as others in the genus.

B. Fantasia, a hybrid, is a perfect size for the window sill with green leaves spotted ivory, green or rose. The pendent inflorescence of scarlet bracts and blue flowers makes it most appealing.

B. horrida has heavily spined gray-banded leaves and an erect spike of greenish petals tipped blue and circled by pink bracts. A very colorful medium-size plant.

B. leptopoda with broad green leaves spotted cream-color rarely grows above 12 inches. Leaf tips curl and the inflorescence has pink bracts and green-and-blue flowers. A good pot plant.

B. lietzei, a charming small plant, will light up your window with bright cerise flowers around the holiday season.

B. meyeri, tall and thin with gray leaves banded with silver produces a trailing pink scape with green-and-blue petals. Grow it on the dry side.

B. nutans, called Queen's Tears, is different in the genus. It has dark-green narrow arching leaves with nodding flower scapes; green-tipped and violet blue. I grow a specimen plant in a big pot; it blazes with color at Christmas. This species grows fast and delights every plant lover.

B. porteana with gray green leaves makes a plant to 36 inches with a cascading scape of pink bracts and green petals. A slow growing but excellent species often confused with *B. zebrina.*

B. pyramidalis var. *concolor* is a favorite with collectors.

BILLBERGIA HYBRID

It is a broad-leafed bottle-shaped plant, golden green. The compact flower head is densely set with pink to red flowers on a short scape. A very beautiful Billbergia that blooms in winter.

B. sanderiana makes a medium-size few-leafed vase. The foliage varies with light exposure from grayish green almost to red. The nodding inflorescence is rose, green, and blue.

B. venezuelana is a big tubular species growing to 40 inches. The leaves are patterned with chocolate-brown and silver bands, a startling combination. The scape is equally bold laden with broad usually pink bracts and purple petals. Needs somewhat dry growing conditions.

B. zebrina is broad-leafed and tubular with gray-green foliage banded with silver, large showy pink bracts and, as a rule, golden flowers in a trailing scape. A handsome Billbergia that puts on a fine show in summer or autumn. This species also requires dry conditions.

Billbergias can be grown under various conditions but they do best with warmth, 60 degrees F. at night in winter, good light and at least a few hours of direct sun. I grow my plants at a south window and they respond well. There are some species like *B. venezuelana* and *B. nutans* that will want sun and others, like *B. amoena* and *B. distachia* that need only bright light and no sun. Some of my Billbergias are in osmunda, others in a terrestrial mix, and most of them are kept in 3- or 4-inch containers.

I do not put my plants outside in summer since they thrive indoors all year and are not as particular about air movement as other Bromeliads. The genus propagates readily by offshoot. Billbergias are of easy culture and most rewarding. By all means, include some in your window garden.

BROMELIA

Bromelia is a genus of about thirty-five terrestrial species found in Mexico and the West Indies to Paraguay and Argentina. Most of the Bromelias are very large plants excellent for outdoor use in temperate climates but not suited for indoor growing. However, a few smaller species are finding their way into cultivation and should be available soon.

These Bromeliads develop large fans of green leaves heavily spined. Bracts are brilliant red and appear lacquered; in bloom, the center of the plant glows with color. The small white flowers are densely set into the inflorescence. I have not grown species in this genus but have seen them in bloom in outdoor gardens where their appearance is always amazing.

B. balansae has spiny, hooked dark-green leaves 4 to 7 feet long with red bracts and a cone-shaped inflorescence of blush-white flowers. At blooming time, the center erupts into a volcano of flame red. A splendid sight.

B. humilis, is smaller, about 2 feet across, with narrow toothed green leaves. The red heart of flame surrounds hidden flowers in the core of the plant.

Pot in a sandy loam mixture in any type container, even cans will do. Although Bromelias can stand full sun, diffused light suits them better. These plants do not have a leaf cup for water storage, so apply moisture frequently and liberally to the soil in warm weather, less in the cool months. Bromelias are excellent landscape plants and can stand 32 degrees F. at night. In boundary plantings, the spiny hooked leaves keep out intruders.

Propagation is by large stolons from the base of the plant,

BROMELIA BALANSAE

and most growers recommend that Bromelias fill their containers with roots so repotting is not needed for years. This genus is not easy to locate, looks notoriously bad when not in flower, is difficult to ship, and is so spiny you have to wear gloves when handling the plants. Even so, all is forgiven when you see them in bloom.

CANISTRUM

Canistrums from Brazil with one species in Trinidad resemble *Neoreglia* and *Nidularium* and are often sold under these names. Seven species represent this genus of rather large tubular or vase-shaped plants. The dark green leaves are toothed and sometimes spotted or banded. The flower head is most attractive, star-shaped and cupped in the center of the plant, sometimes rising above the foliage and sometimes set low in the crown. Flowers are pink-and-white.

My plants of *C. fosterianum* and *C. lindeni* var. *lindeni* make excellent indoor subjects. They are not as easy to grow as some other Bromeliads but the handsome foliage makes them highly decorative. Where space is available, I certainly recommend a few Canistrums.

C. fosterianum grows to 16 inches with grayish green mottled leaves. The large flower head is raised and surrounded with brilliant pink bracts, a very handsome species.

C. lindeni var. *lindeni* of medium size, has light green leaves spotted dark green. The rose-shaped inflorescence has white bracts and is either sunk in the cup or rises well above it. Usually summer flowering.

C. lindeni var. *roseum* is a larger plant with rose-colored bracts and white-and-green flowers.

C. lindeni var. *viride* has green bracts and is perhaps the handsomest of this group but not yet readily available.

Canistrums are still rare in cultivation and information on growing them is scarce. I keep my plants moderately moist throughout the year and at a west window where they receive some indirect sunlight. They are placed in back of some large orchid plants. After two years, these Canistrums are healthy and growing but have not bloomed yet. Even so, they are most decorative. This is a good genus for those who enjoy experimenting.

CATOPSIS

Catopsis is a genus with about twenty-five species, from the West Indies and southern Mexico to Peru. These smooth-leaved epiphytic Bromeliads have an erect or arching scape with attractive small yellow or white flowers. They are medium size growers, mostly bottle-shaped, and make excellent house plants. Only a few species are available at present but I'm sure we will see more in the future. My collection includes *C. berteroniana*, *C. floribunda*, *C. morreniana*, and *C. nutans*.

I am particularly fond of the Catopsis species because they grow with little care and the small ones make handsome table decorations used pot and all. Although they are slow growing, I think you may enjoy a few in your window garden.

C. berteroniana, a medium-size plant, has apple-green leaves, green bracts and small white flowers that usually appear in the spring.

C. floribunda is a small bushy bottle-shaped plant with

11

CATOPSIS FLORIBUNDA

bright green foliage and pretty white flowers on a tall arching spike that appears in spring. Excellent for the beginner.

C. *morreniana* is a small delicate looking plant with a branched inflorescence. A pretty species.

C. *nutans* grows only 7 inches high with broad pointed leaves. The small flowers are bright yellow.

These Bromeliads do best in osmunda in 3- or 4-inch pots but can also be grown on tree-fern slabs. My plants in average home temperatures are at a west window. Water heavily and then allow drying out before wetting again. Culture with Catopsis species is very much like that for Orchids.

These epiphytes are excellent for the home because they require little attention. Grow them out of the sun but in diffused light.

CRYPTANTHUS

Cryptanthus is a genus of terrestrial Bromeliads found in eastern Brazil. They grow on the forest floor in shade or in full sun. Mostly small plants, they are valued for their multicolored foliage. However, I find the small white flowers also attractive and desirable because as one flower fades, another opens and it is possible for one Cryptanthus to be in bloom for more than two weeks.

These Bromeliads are without equal for decorative accent as border color outside or as fill-in for plant arrangements indoors. There are about twenty species available with C. *zonatus* and C. *bivittatus* the best known. Cryptanthus plants are inexpensive and handsome and can be purchased from most large florists. I grow about a dozen kinds.

Generally the leaves form a rosette that suggests a star. Because these are mainly small plants, Cryptanthus species are

CRYPTANTHUS SPECIES

ideal for the window sill. Many unusual hybrids with purple or red or bronze foliage have been introduced recently. Sometimes overlooked because they lack colorful flowers, these Bromeliads are well worth space in the home or in the temperate garden.

C. *acaulis* grows about 5 inches across, the pointed leaves apple-green with a slight gray overcast. Tiny white flowers hide deep in the center of the plant.

C. *beuckeri* is slightly different in the genus with green-and-cream spoon-shaped leaves.

C. *bivittatus*, sometimes sold as C. *roseus pictus*, is perhaps the most common, frequently used in dish gardens because of the spectacular salmon-rose and olive-green leaves.

C. *bromelioides* grows 12 to 14 inches high. Leaves are copper-red in sun, gray-green in shade. Very easy to grow.

C. *bromelioides* var. *tricolor* is my favorite in the genus. It is larger than most species with pointed upright highly-colored leaves about 12 inches long. They are striped and lined lengthwise with white, rose and olive-green. Sometimes called the Rainbow Plant.

C. *fosterianus*, about 14 inches tall, has thick stiff brown leaves with zigzag crossbands.

C. *zonatus*, a small species, has broad wavy brownish green leaves crossbanded with irregular silver markings. The white flowers are hidden in the leaf axils.

Cryptanthus plants require a terrestrial mix and most species do well in a 2- or 3-inch pot. However, a group can be put directly into osmunda and sphagnum for a planter combination. These plants grow in any light place but not in full shade. Because they like a moist atmosphere, I water them heavily in spring and summer but only about once a week through the rest of the year. A terrarium is an excellent showplace for Cryptanthus plants; they are small enough to be handsome in such a housing, and they thrive there.

Offshoots are produced in an unusual way. After the blooming, plantlets grow on axils between the leaves in the manner of the spider plant. When half-grown, the plantlets can be pinched off and separately potted. Some species also produce new growth on stolons.

DYCKIA

Dyckia is a genus of some seventy species from Bolivia, Uruguay, Paraguay, parts of Argentina, and a great many growing in the dry open campos of Brazil. With spiny sharp-pointed leaves, these plants are easily mistaken for cactus. There are small, medium, and giant types, and a few of the smaller Dyckias will enhance any collection.

The tall flower spike is usually branched with small, pretty pink, orange, or yellow blooms. Under my conditions, these terrestrials are not as easily grown as other Bromeliads. Direct sun, about four hours a day, is necessary and water must be carefully given.

The small Dyckias are excellent for rock gardens in areas where temperatures do not drop below 50 degrees. Some species like *D. brevifolia* and *D. rariflora* are good as borders for indoor plants, or you might like them in a terrarium grouping. I have *D. brevifolia, D. fosteriana, D. leptostachya* and *D. rariflora*.

D. brevifolia, once known as *D. sulphurea*, grows 10 to 15 inches across with stiff succulent dark green leaves. The tall spray of orange flowers appears at various times. Will do wonderfully in the garden and can take some light frost.

D. fosteriana is the most popular species and rightly so. It makes a handsome medium-size plant with silvery purple

DYCKIA FOSTERIANA (above)
DYCKIA BREVIFOLIA (below)

1. Window tray of Bromeliad species.

2. Terrarium with Cryptanthus species.

3. Floor Planter.

4. *Aechmea fasciata*, dependable for summer bloom.

5. *Guzmania monostachia* bright red in late winter.

6. Star-shaped *Guzmania magnifica*.

7. Small Bromeliad, *Aechmea mertensii*, color from October to April.

8. *Tillandsia* species Fantastic Gardens, Miami, Florida.

9. Handsome, lush *Neoregelia carolinae*.

10. Small bright-colored *Quesnelia humilis*.

11. Queen's Tears *Billbergia nutans*, for winter flowers.

12. Striking *Aechmea chantinii*, king of the Bromeliads for April color.

13. *Nidularium innocentii striatum* produces white flowers in summer.

14. *Guzmania lingulata* with high flower crown.

15. *Guzmania vittata* with driftwood.

16. Amazing *Tillandsia ionantha*, small and colorful in early spring.

17. *Aechmea pubescens*, colorful in winter.

18. *Guzmania* hybrid, one of the best species in the genus.

rosettes that cascade over the pot, recurve, and form a fountain of leaves. Small orange flowers appear in spring or summer.

D. frigida is a big plant with spiny recurved leaves. The narrow stalk is branched and produces small but very pretty orange flowers.

D. leptostachya, a medium-size species has reddish brown foliage and attractive orange flowers.

D. rariflora is small with gray-green foliage and orange flowers.

Use a terrestrial potting mix with a good amount of sand; small pots are best and direct sun a necessity. Although Dyckias should supposedly be grown on the dry side, I find that liberal soakings followed by a drying-out period suit them better.

Do not propagate Dyckias, rather let them grow into specimen plants. Because of the spiny leaves, wear gloves when handling plants. Although this genus is difficult, a healthy plant in bloom is a rewarding sight.

GRAVISIA

Gravisias with some six species are epiphytes found in Costa Rica, Jamaica, Trinidad, and Venezuela. These large plants are urn-shaped, have stiff broad leaves and resemble Aechmeas. The branched scapes blaze with orange-and-yellow flowers.

These Bromeliads are excellent for garden or patio in areas where temperatures do not go below freezing. They can also be grown in the house provided they have some warm months outside. *G. aquilega* and *G. fosteriana* are recent additions to my collection.

G. aquilega has light green leaves and bears tufted heads of orange-yellow flowers cupped in rose bracts like miniature bouquets. Scapes are sometimes 30 to 40 inches tall.

G. fosteriana has stiff yellow-green foliage with tiny spines. The branched inflorescence has pink bracts with clusters of orange-and-yellow flowers.

Other than these two species, Gravisias are not common in cultivation and little is known about growing them. I use a crushed gravel and soil mix in 3- or 4-inch pots depending upon plant size. Allow a drying-out between liberal waterings and grow these species on the warm side, 65 degrees F. at night in winter.

This is an exciting genus to me because there is much to learn about it and the Gravisias I have seen in flower are appealing and worth the extra effort.

GREIGIA

Greigias with about twenty species from Colombia and Ecuador, a few from Chile and Mexico, are terrestrial Bromeliads. They enjoy cool moist conditions and do well in the Midwest. These large plants are rather like Bromelias with spiny leaves. Unlike most Bromeliads, they bear flowers from the axils of the leaves instead of from the center of the plant. The two species I have are in good health but have yet to bloom. These plants were given to me by a friend in South America and are not identified.

Other than from amateur growers in Florida or California, I doubt whether these plants are available but I imagine we will see some in the future for they are good pot plants for partial sun and cool temperatures, about 56 degrees F. at night in winter. I use a terrestrial mix for Greigias and keep them on the dry side.

GUZMANIA

Guzmanias are a handsome group of mostly epiphytic Bromeliads from the Andean rain forests. Some species are also found in southern Florida, the West Indies, Venezuela, Brazil, and Central America. Leaves are glossy, smooth edged, and in a rosette. The inflorescence is perhaps the most beautiful of all Bromeliads, highly colored and long lasting. The spike is produced from the center of the plant and in most species rises well above the foliage. Some of the species have excellent leaf color.

I have grown G. *berteroniana*, G. *Magnifica*, G. *musaica*, G. *lingulata*, G. *monostachia*, G. *vittata*, and G. *zahni* with success. These easy-to-grow plants are mainly spring and summer flowering.

G. *berteroniana* is medium size with leaves to 20 inches. The showy inflorescence has orange-red bracts with yellow flowers. A fine plant for the window sill.

G. *lingulata* is a handsome species about 18 inches across with a star-shaped, orange flower head. G. *Peacocki* (G. *lingulata*. var. *splendens*) has bronze-rose leaves and G. *lingulata* var. *minor*, a red-orange inflorescence with white flowers.

G. *Magnifica* is a hybrid and a good one for the beginner. Its graceful rosette of leaves is decorative and the red flower head is star-shaped and forms lower in the crown than in most species of the group.

G. *monostachia* (G. *monstachya*) is of medium size, about 24 inches across. The satiny green leaves are narrow and ar-

GUZMANIA BERTERONIANA

GUZMANIA VITTATA

ranged in a dense rosette. The poker-like flower spike is erect with white flowers and green bracts stenciled with maroon lines. The very tip of the inflorescence is crowned blood red in many varieties, orange in others. A very showy Bromeliad.

G. musaica is sure to please house-plant enthusiasts. The leaves are 24 inches long, bright green, banded and overlayed with irregular lines of dark green and wavy purple markings on the reverse. The flower spike is erect and turns red at flowering time. The white waxy flowers are set tight into the poker-shaped flower head.

G. vittata is a medium-size plant with graceful pointed, soft green leaves barred with maroon on the reverse. The handsome foliage makes it valuable for every collection but it also produces a round, white flower head with greenish bracts edged purple. Even at the darkest window, this fine plant retains decorative leaves. Don't grow below 60 degrees F.

G. zahni grows to 20 inches, the delicate leaves almost transparent and striped red-brown. The flower spike has bright red bracts and white flowers that hold color for 6 to 8 weeks.

Osmunda is the best potting material for Guzmanias and 4- or 5-inch pots adequate. These plants do best at a west window and direct sun should be avoided. Grow all species warmer than most other Bromeliads with a minimum of 62 degrees at night in winter. High humidity, at least 50 per cent, and a free circulation of warm air are essential for these handsome plants.

Propagation is by offshoots, generally after flowering.

HECHTIA

Hechtias, mainly from Mexico are Bromeliads that strongly resemble cacti. There are small, medium and large species, the majority with colorful saw-toothed foliage. Smaller Hechtias are frequently used for dish gardens. To my way of thinking the larger types with long erect flower spikes belong outdoors, where they are exceptionally beautiful. All of them require full sun. My collection includes *H. rosea* and *H. texensis*. *H. argentea* and *H. glomerata* are also available.

H. argentea has large recurved leaves in a symmetrical rosette with a tall spike of orange flowers. A good showy Bromeliad.

H. glomerata is a small to medium plant with fleshy green recurved leaves armed with spines.

H. rosea is very decorative. It has reddish bronze spiny leaves and produces hundreds of tiny pink flowers on a tall scape in October for me. My favorite in the group.

H. texensis with rosettes of sharp saw-toothed green leaves is a small grower and best suited for a dish garden.

A sandy terrestrial mix and 3- or 4-inch pots are needed for Hechtias. Keep plants on the dry side during the cold months but increase waterings in warmer weather. My plants are at an east window all year where there is direct sun. Watering these species is a problem because of the recurved nature of the leaves and the spiny edges. Handle with care to avoid cuts.

Recently, large Hechtias have been used successfully in landscaping in warm countries; they are decorative here and much easier to grow than in the indoor garden. It is best not to propagate them, rather, let them grow into specimen plants.

16

HECHTIA ROSEA

HOHENBERGIA

Hohenbergias with vase-shaped growth are mostly terrestrial Bromeliads from Guatemala, the West Indies, and Venezuela. There are only two species available, both giant plants but certainly worth the space. In good light the foliage is vibrant yellow-green, almost golden, and the tall branched inflorescence has tufted crowns of red and purple. Summering outdoors is necessary for these exceptional plants.

I grow *H. stellata* and *H. ridleyi* indoors at east windows from September to May. In warm weather, I set them on an open back porch in almost full sun where they are a handsome sight indeed against a wall of natural brick. Usually summer blooming, these Bromeliads can't be beat for patios.

H. ridleyi grows to 5 feet with golden yellow leaves and a tall branched red-and-purple inflorescence.

H. stellata has 3 to 5 foot spiny leaves and a tall spike with red bracts and purple flowers. An outstanding sight in any garden.

Usually growing on rocks or in the ground, Hohenbergias need a terrestrial mix. Large pots, 8- to 10-inches are best and perfect drainage essential. Avoid tight packing at the base of the plant for this can cause death. It is best to buy these species potted and let them grow into specimens. Moderate waterings and temperatures are required.

Leaf color depends upon sunlight and Hohenbergias should not be grown where natural light is limited.

17

HOHENBERGIA STELLATA

NEOREGELIA

Neoregelias are epiphytic and terrestrial plants from eastern Brazil, Peru and eastern Colombia. Most species make excellent house plants that can survive neglect. Dense clusters of small blue-and-white flowers form in the center of the plants but it is the color of the foliage before blooming that is most spectacular. The area around the core turns brilliant red. Leaf color varies from apple-green to dark green to maroon. Foliage is banded with color or mottled, or in many species, red-tipped. Hence the name Painted Fingernail Plants.

Most Neoregelias are of medium-size with spreading leaf rosettes but there are also smaller species. I grow *N. ampullacea, N. carolinae, N. carolinae tricolor, N. cruenta, N. johannis, N. Marmorata* and *N. spectabilis* and find them outstanding decorative plants for the home. They can be used in planter groupings, separately, or on low tables. Try a few; they are sure to please you.

N. ampullacea, about 9 inches across, has leaves with mahogany crossbands and small blue flowers in spring or summer. Give a little more light than for most Neoregelias.

N. carolinae is perhaps the showiest in the genus, the tapered leaves dark green, the center of the plant bright red before blooming. My plant was in full color for nine months. Undoubtedly one of the finest house plants obtainable.

N. carolinae var. *tricolor* is expensive but a panorama of color; the variegated leaves white-striped. When in flower the foliage has a pinkish hue and the heart of the plant turns cerise. A highly desirable Bromeliad that steals the show. Grow it in shade with warmth.

NEOREGELIA JOHANNIS

N. cruenta forms a medium-size upright rosette with straw-colored leaves edged with red spines. A most unusual Neoregelia that needs full sun.

N. johannis is a durable species with a lavender center. Although not as handsome as others in the genus, it is still worthwhile.

N. Marmorata is a hybrid with yellow-green and crimson leaves. Spring or winter flowering, it needs good light for proper leaf color. Flowers are white and deep in the cup. This one seems to thrive on neglect. It's for people who "can't grow anything."

N. spectabilis, specifically the Painted Fingernail Plant, has spine-free leathery green leaves tipped cerise. The small blue flowers usually appear in warm weather.

Some of my Neoregelias are potted in a terrestrial compost, others in osmunda. All do well provided there is good drainage. Medium-size pots, say 4-inch, suit most species. Light requirements vary, although most Neoregelias tolerate semishade. Move your plants around until you find a happy spot for them. Leaf color gives the clue.

These air plants are not fussy about humidity or air circulation and will grow easily under average home conditions. Propagation is by offshoot after flowering.

NIDULARIUM

Nidulariums grow in the rain forests of Brazil under shady damp conditions. Most species are handsome and excellent subjects for those orphan north windows where very few green plants survive. And prior to blooming, the inner periphery of foliage turns fiery red to brighten those gray exposures. There are many species that are of medium size, the leaves

19

NIDULARIUM FULGENS

arranged in a dense rosette. The small red or white or blue flowers are low in the cup of the plant and only in a few species rise above the plant. Looking down at them, they remind me of tiny water lilies and, although the flowers are short-lived, the scarlet around the cup holds color for six months.

The thirty species of these epiphytes are easy to grow; they are perfect house plants for those who have little time for plants but enjoy some living color at their windows. I have eight Nidularium species, all willing subjects, all healthy. Try a few of these.

N. billbergioides is small and one of the few species that produces a flower head on a 6- to 8-inch stalk. The leaves are green, the bracts orange; tiny white flowers appear in summer or fall. Another available form is *N. billbergioides* var. *citrinum*. This has a bright yellow secondary rosette.

N. fulgens with pale green leaves spotted dark green displays a bright cerise leaf cup at blooming time, which is usually in spring. A very decorative plant.

N. innocentii var. *innocentii* makes a large plant with almost purple leaves. The white flowers nestle deep in a rusty red cup.

N. innocentii var. *striatum* has creamy white-and-green striped leaves, a flaming red center and white flowers in summer. This species is somewhat temperamental and requires warmth.

N. innocentii var. *wittmackiana* has green leaves and small white flowers in winter or spring.

N. procerum is big with long yellow-green leaves. The bright red cup holds orange-red flowers; a very handsome color combination.

N. regelioides, one of the first Bromeliads I bought, makes a compact rosette with dark green leathery leaves. The flowers are red.

Nidulariums do well in a terrestrial mix or potted in osmunda. Although most species like warmth, they will also tolerate temperatures to 55 degrees with the exception of the *N. innocentii* varieties. I have my plants at a northern exposure where humidity averages 40 to 60 per cent. Keep the foliage clean and sparkling by sponging with water now and then.

These species of Bromeliads endure more neglect than any other house plant I know. They are recommended for decoration on coffee tables or low chests, almost anyplace in the home. Start with Nidulariums; they will quickly make you a Bromeliad enthusiast.

ORTHOPHYTUM

Orthophytum is a genus of terrestrial Bromeliads from Brazil with cactuslike growth. Although not spectacular, it is an interesting group with several decorative species that do well in the home. They are medium or small plants grown for their colorful foliage; the tiny white flowers that appear in summer or fall are insignificant. You probably would not want more than one or two species from this genus. I grow *O. fosterianum* and *O. vagans*. *O. navoides* and *O. saxicola* are also worthwhile.

O. fosterianum is medium size with apple green leathery leaves edged with spines. It bears tufted flower crowns at the leaf axils. A very different Bromeliad; the best in the group.

O. navioides with narrow arching leaves makes a handsome rosette. It is small and good for a window sill.

O. saxicola has small white flowers and broad pointed leaves armed with spines.

O. vagans, only 10 inches tall, is a beauty in bloom; the top

ORTHOPHYTUM FOSTERIANUM

leaves of the plant are covered with what looks like red lacquer and small white flowers dot the crown in October.

Orthophytums require a terrestrial mix with some crushed stone or gravel. Use 2- or 3-inch pots and water heavily; then allow a drying-out before wetting again.

Some sun is necessary so a west or south exposure is ideal. Do try *O. fosterianum* and *O. vagans;* they are unusual and attractive.

PITCAIRNIA

Pitcairnia is a genus of about seventy terrestrial or rock-growing species from Mexico and the West Indies to northern Argentina, with one species found in Africa. Most Pitcairnias are fairly large plants with graceful tapered leaves and a showy inflorescence, usually red. These Bromeliads are desirable where a vertical accent is needed in decoration.

The leaves are grayish-green and the erect branched flower stalk rises well above the foliage. Somewhat difficult, the Pitcairnias are of different growth from most Bromeliads. Although flowers last only a few days, the plants are very beautiful and worthwhile. The entire spike can be cut and used effectively for a vase arrangement. *P. paniculata* and *P. corallina* are favorites in my collection and *P. andreana*, a dwarf species is a real gem.

P. andreana is perfect for the window sill. It is 10 inches high and bears pretty yellow and orange flowers in early spring.

P. corallina, the most common cultivated species, grows to 36 inches with a pendent flower spike and coral red blossoms. Although difficult to grow, this Pitcairnia is a delight in bloom.

21

PITCAIRNIA ANDREANA

PITCAIRNIA PANICULATA

P. paniculata, a large fast growing plant has an erect spike with brilliant red-and-yellow flowers. A very attractive species that blooms in early October for me.

I pot Pitcairnias in a well-aerated terrestrial mix with a good amount of sand. They grow well in large coffee cans and I have not disturbed them. (The dwarf species thrives in a 2-inch pot.) In spring and summer these plants require quantities of water and, unlike most Bromeliads, do well with additional fertilizer (10-10-5) about once a month. Taper off watering in cold weather.

Temperature and humidity make little difference to these species but I grow them on the cool side, 54 degrees F. at night in winter. A south or west window offers good light. Although only a few species are now available, we are likely to have more of these fine Bromeliads in the future.

PORTEA

Porteas from Brazil include a few species that are most decorative. Medium or large, these species are vase- or bottle-shaped and the inflorescence is dense and colorful. I grow *P. kermesina* but it is *P. petropolitana* var. *extensa* that steals the show when it is in bloom. This large plant is one of the showiest of the Bromeliads and should certainly be grown where there is ample space.

P. kermesina is of medium size with pink flowers on an erect branched stalk.

P. petropolitana var. *extensa* has large spreading yellow-green leaves heavily edged with purple spines. The tubular pink, green and lavender flowers are in a branched raceme; a remarkable combination of colors, followed by blue-lavender berries that last for months.

PORTEA PETROPOLITANA VAR EXTENSA

I recommend Porteas for indoor growing. Use large containers, depending upon the size of the plants; a west exposure is fine. These Bromeliads need moderate humidity, about 45 per cent. Grow them somewhat on the warm side, never below 60 degrees F. at night in winter.

The branched stalks of *P. petropolitana* can be cut and placed in a vase of water for a handsome table decoration.

PUYA

Puyas come principally from Chile with some species in Costa Rica, British Guiana, Brazil, and parts of Argentina. In their habitat, some species grow to 50 feet and bear thousands of flowers. However, there are some small to medium species available that make good fill-in plants for dish gardens and larger types that are excellent for outdoors in temperate areas. Most species have narrow leaves armed with sharp spines; the flower stalk is produced from the center of the plant.

P. alpestris is large size with sharp narrow recurved leaves. The branched inflorescence is blue and green. A real beauty.

P. berteroniana is also large and handsome with green-and-blue flowers. Outside it will withstand 30 degree temperatures.

P. chilensis is a big plant with a tall branched flower stalk; this one should be grown outdoors. A really colorful Bromeliad in bloom with hundreds of green-and-yellow flowers.

These terrestrial and rock-growing Bromeliads need a sandy loam mixture with some crushed stone at the bottom of the pot. The Puyas are sun lovers and best for the patio or garden rather than in the home.

I find that the two species I grow need more water indoors

than one expects for such desert-looking Bromeliads. The Puyas withstand a temperature range from 32 to well over 100 degrees and in general survive considerable neglect. It is hard to appreciate this genus until you see the plants growing in their native soil; they bear gigantic flower stalks reaching high toward the sky and crowned with colorful flowers.

QUESNELIA

Quesnelias from Brazil are handsome Bromeliads of small to large species. In general, the foliage is decorative, the flowers lavender-blue, red-purple or pink. Although they are difficult to bring into bloom, they are well worth the effort.

Most species do well under adversity and are ideal for apartment growing even though they may not bloom. I grow *Q. arvensis, Q. humilis* and *Q. liboniana*. There are many other species available.

Q. arvensis is to me the most striking plant in the genus with its large bushy crossbanded foliage. The inflorescence is a vivid red cone stuffed with blue-and-white flowers.

Q. humilis is delightful, about 10 inches tall. The light blue flowers are produced on a short arching scape in April on my plant; an excellent species.

Q. liboniana has a tubular form and grows to 30 inches. The branched inflorescence is red and blue; another handsome house plant.

Q. quesneliana is a large stiff vase-shaped species with a tufted flower crown on an erect stem. A good Bromeliad if you have the room for it.

I use osmunda and 5- or 6-inch containers depending on plant size. I give warmth, 65 degrees F. at night in winter, and 40 to 60 per cent humidity.

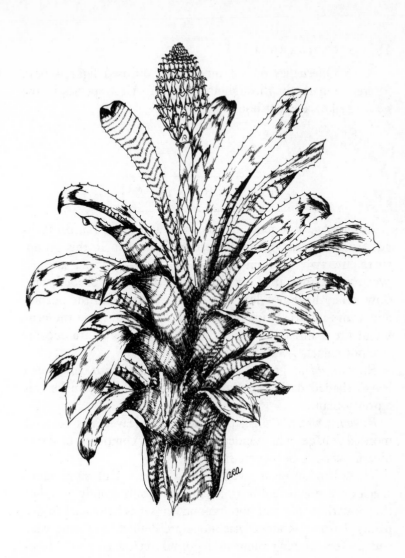

QUESNELIA ARVENSIS

Keep Quesnelias out of direct sun; diffused light is best. Water moderately throughout the year. Most species in the genus make excellent house plants.

RONNBERGIA

Ronnbergia is a genus of epiphytic and terrestrial Bromeliads from Panama and southwestern Colombia. In this group, there are two medium-size plants, *R. columbiana* and *R. morreniana*, that are ideal for a cool somewhat shaded window. They have few leaves in a funnel shape and the purple-and-white inflorescence is produced in a spike from the center of the plant. Even out of bloom, both species are decorative pot plants.

R. columbiana grows 12 to 16 inches high with dark green leaves shaded dark red. Purple-and-white flowers make this a pretty plant.

R. morreniana, a small plant with few leaves, has colorful mottled foliage. The slender erect scape is composed of dense blue flowers. A handsome species.

These Bromeliads do well in the Midwest; I am sorry more species are not in cultivation. The cool and cloudy weather that is with us most of autumn and winter is beneficial to my plants. I water Ronnbergias moderately all through the year and prefer growing them in a porous terrestrial mix. However, osmunda is satisfactory for potting, too.

Grow these plants at a west or north window and provide as much humidity as possible; they will not do well under arid conditions. Cool nights, 55 degrees F. in winter, are needed and it is best to grow Ronnbergias out of direct sun. In hot weather, mist plants daily with water.

STREPTOCALYX

Streptocalyx is a genus of decorative Bromeliads from French Guiana, Brazil, Ecuador, Peru, Bolivia and Colombia. Leaves are narrow and arching in a heavy rosette and bright rose-colored flower heads are spectacular. *S. longifolia* and *S. poeppigii* are welcome additions to my collection.

These epiphytes are not dependable about blooming and to insure better health and possibility of flowers I suggest summering plants outdoors. They are mainly summer and fall flowering.

S. longifolia is of medium size with a dense rosette of spiny leaves. The ovoid inflorescence is a whitish-rose color on a short scape.

S. poeppigii is large with narrow spiny coppery-red leaves. This is a handsome foliage plant that bears an erect scape crowned with a cylindrical head of densely-set red or rose-purple flowers followed by pink-and-white berries. These gradually change to purple and last for months. Leaf color varies according to light exposure. An essential species for the Bromeliad enthusiast.

Pot Streptocalyx in osmunda in large pots, 5- to 7-inches, and allow them to grow into specimens. A west exposure is best with some sunshine. Grow them somewhat dry except in summer when they can take liberal watering. Although these Bromeliads are easy to grow, they do not flower regularly. Rain water and more sunlight may be the answer.

STREPTOCALYX POEPPIGII

TILLANDSIA

Tillandsia with more than four hundred species is the largest genus in the Bromeliaceae. It also has the widest distribution, growing in the southeastern United States and to northern Argentina and Chile. This group has been overlooked by the home-garden enthusiast and yet it offers many remarkable easy-to-grow flowering subjects. I have a *T. ionantha* that is truly amazing; it grows and blooms regularly spending its life on the top of the fir bark of an orchid pot capturing moisture through the leaf cells.

Tillandsias range in size from miniature 1-inch species to giants. Epiphytes, they vary greatly in growth, flower form, and leaf color and design. There are Tillandsias to please everyone but because there are so many it is important to choose carefully. Some species have insignificant flowers, others are showy. Many have decorative foliage, some are plain green. Some Tillandsias do not take kindly to indoor growing while others do very well. Many are excellent for gardens, so selection is important. It is a matter of taste and where you want to use the plant that will determine which species to buy. Here is a list of dependable Tillandsias that I have grown in my home. A few of these species will surely do well in your indoor garden.

T. anceps is a small stemless species with numerous arching leaves and a large ovoid inflorescence, pale green or rose with blue petals.

T. brachycaulos is handsome with many leaves. At blooming time, the center foliage turns from green to coppery red with purple flowers. Mount this species on a slab of tree fern.

T. bulbosa has a bulbous base with narrow leathery leaves.

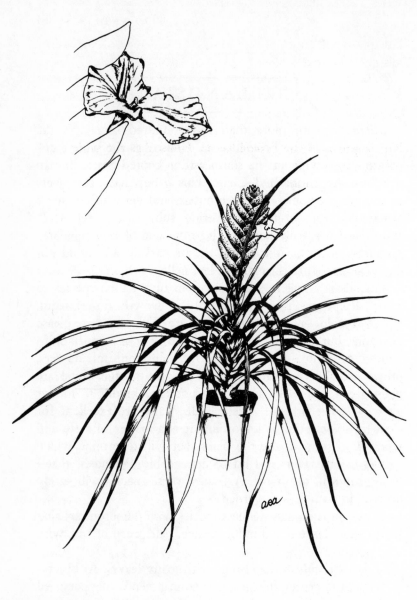

TILLANDSIA CYANEA

The inflorescence is pretty, magenta and white. An oddity best grown out of a pot on a piece of bark or branch.

T. butzii is small with thin twisted cylindrical leaves that are purple spotted. The bracts are rose colored with purple petals and yellow stamens. A pretty species that blooms in spring.

T. caput-medusae resembles *T. bulbosa*, small with vivid blue flowers.

T. cyanea, one of the most popular Tillandsias and rightly so, is a regal plant with graceful arching leaves resembling a palm. From the center of this medium-size species, an erect flower stalk bears a feathery pink sword of large purple-shaded flowers—a stunning Bromeliad that needs moisture and humidity to bloom. This is one of the more difficult ones to grow at home but well worth trying.

T. fasciculata is medium size with blue or purple flowers. Among the many varieties available, leaf and flower color vary somewhat. A good one for the beginner.

T. flexuosa, sometimes called *T. aloifolia*, has coppery-green twisted leaves with silver crossbands. It bears red bracts and white flowers.

T. geminiflora, a dense rosette of green leaves, has a branched inflorescence and is a good plant for a Bromeliad tree. An easy species and most decorative.

T. ionantha is a dwarf hardly more than 2 inches high but it will astound you at blooming time in spring when all the leaves blush fiery red and the pretty purple flower pokes its head through the foliage. Grow it in sun or bright light; it needs little care.

T. juncea is small and pretty with narrow leaves in a tufted growth and a red flower crown. A favorite of mine.

T. lindenii is similar to *T. cyanea* with long graceful tapered reddish-green leaves. The inflorescence is pink and blue. A real beauty but difficult to bloom.

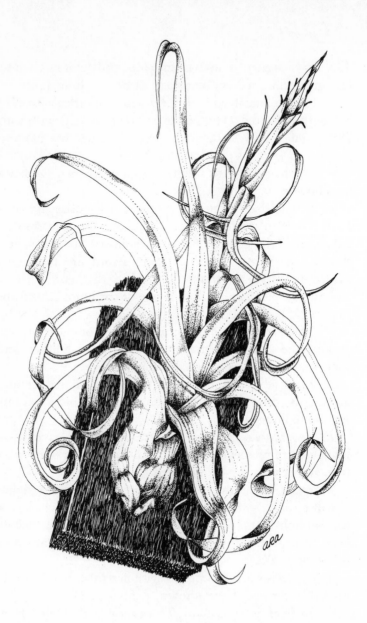

TILLANDSIA STREPTOPHYLLA

T. paraensis grows to 7 inches and is a good window-sill plant. Leaves are grayish green, the flower bracts pink.

T. punctulata with narrow silver-gray pointed leaves bears a heavy inflorescence that is densely set with rose-red bracts and purple-and-white flowers. A good small air plant.

T. streptophylla is medium size with a bulbous base and grayish green curving foliage. The inflorescence is branched, almost the same color as the leaves, with pink bracts. A mature specimen is a handsome sight.

T. tricolor with grayish-green leaves edged red is of medium size. The pink-and-red inflorescence is upright and branched rising well above the plant.

I grow fifteen Tillandsia species and after much trial and error, I find they do better on tree-fern slabs (available at orchid supply centers) or affixed to pieces of tree branches rather than in pots. (The exceptions are *T. cyanea* and *T. lindenii* which I grow in containers.) The slabs are dunked into a bucket of water for about fifteen minutes every third day in hot weather, about once a week the rest of the year. I spray Tillandsias with a fine mist of water any time I happen to pass them; they appreciate as much humidity as you can give them. Most of my species grow well at a west window where they get some sun. *T. cyanea* and *T. lindenii* are at a north exposure.

The smaller species mentioned here are good subjects for dish gardens or Bromeliad trees or even for terrariums with ample air circulation. Tillandsias are inexpensive, plentiful, and many many other species not mentioned here can also be tried indoors.

VRIESEA

Vriesea, a spectacular genus from Mexico to the West Indies to Argentina, includes many large, showy plants. Epiphytes with dense rosettes of smooth-edged leaves, they have a brilliant erect, sometimes branched inflorescence shaped like a shell or fan and with a waxy texture that enhances the vivid color. At times, they hardly seem real.

The Vrieseas make excellent graceful pot plants, the flower heads holding color for months. In general, they are easy to grow, and many species are available from the more than 150 in cultivation today. Most Vrieseas do not like bright sun and so they are willing subjects for orphan north windows. Beside the larger types, there are many useful small growers. These are the species I have grown; there are many others.

V. barilletii with a rosette of shiny green leaves bears an erect yellow-and-red inflorescence that is colorful from December to April. Not as showy as most species but very dependable.

V. carinata is small and good for a window sill. It has light green leaves and a flat sword-shaped red-and-yellow flower head.

V. carinata Mariae, the Painted Feather plant is a hybrid and somewhat larger than *V. carinata*. It holds color all winter.

V. fenestralis, a regal plant with green leaves delicately figured darker green and purple lined, is big and bushy but worth the space it takes; a most desirable Bromeliad with yellow flowers. Grow this one warm.

V. heliconoides shouts with color, the flower spike bright

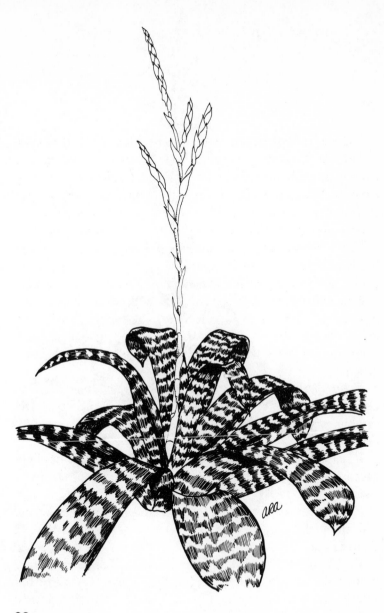

28
VRIESEA HIEROGLYPHICA

VRIESEA MALZINEI

VRIESEA SCHWACKEANA

red edged with charteuse and the green leaves suffused with red—a spectacular plant in bloom.

V. hieroglyphica with rosettes of light green, crossbanded dark green and purple-brown beneath makes a fine decorative plant. The yellow flowers appear in spring on a tall branched spike. Grow this species at a northern exposure with assured humidity.

V. imperialis is very large with green or dark wine-red leaves crowned with a tall branch of red-and-yellow inflorescence. A majestic Bromeliad that requires space.

V. malzinei with a compact rosette of claret-colored leaves shaded green rarely grows above 16 inches and is fine for the window sill. Early in spring the cylindrical flower head has yellow bracts with green margins. A very easy to grow plant.

V. perfecta is the most popular species but not half as showy as others I grow. It has apple-green foliage and produces a yellow-and-red flower spike.

V. petropolitana is a charmer. Only 10 inches high, it bears brilliant orange-and-yellow flowers in early spring.

V. schwackeana is of medium size with green leaves and a strong scape of four to six dark red-and-yellow ovoid heads. Blooming time is spring.

V. splendens var. *splendens*, another good Vriesea grows about 12 inches high, and is a perfect house plant. The green foliage is mahogany striped and the thin thrusting spring and summer inflorescence is orange-colored.

Mainly epiphytes, Vrieseas do best in osmunda potted firm but not tight, and for my plants I use 3- 4- or 5-inch pots. This is a valued genus in my plant room where most of the species grow at a north window beside my shade-loving Orchids. In general, Vrieseas do not like sunshine but do need light. I water these plants every third day except in winter; about once a week then. Vase cups are kept full of water except in very cold weather.

Although Vrieseas are often considered more difficult to grow at home than Aechmeas or Billbergias, I find them easy. I maintain a 60-degree F. minimum temperature at night in winter and good daytime humidity, about 50 per cent. It's a good idea to mist the foliage on hot summer days; this is good for most Bromeliads. Circulation of air is always essential.

Because Vrieseas do not like direct sunshine, I summer very few outdoors; these are against a brick wall facing west. I do not propagate Vrieseas; most species produce offshoots that eventually choke off the mother plant and take hold of the best growing area in the pot.

In this remarkable family, most species hold their colorful flower spikes for three to four months, a great advantage for indoor gardeners. Smaller types of Vrieseas are ideal for planters in the living room where light is often limited. There are many species available and most of them are inexpensive.

WITTROCKIA

Wittrockia from Brazil includes two excellent species. Similar to *Nidularium* and *Neoreglia*, these medium-size plants are still rare in cultivation but more will surely be available. They are not difficult to grow in the home if a little additional humidity is provided. I grow both *W. amazonica* and *W. superba*.

These are compact Bromeliads with spreading rosettes of leaves. The inflorescence is either sunk in the cup of the plant or rises above it with a dense crown and central foliage also coloring at blooming time.

W. amazonica is of medium size, the flower head sunk in the center of the rosette.

31

WITTROCKIA SUPERBA

W. superba with leaves to 24 inches has dark green foliage handsomely tipped red. The inflorescence is slightly raised.

These Bromeliads require a terrestrial mix or osmunda in small pots. They thrive at north or west windows. Water moderately all year and be sure to keep leaf-cups filled. Mist occasionally and avoid a close atmosphere.

Although Wittrockias are not showy they do have a quiet charm. I think you will want one or two for your collection.

APPENDIX

BROMELIADS AT A GLANCE

† terrestrial (species unmarked considered epiphytes though some adapt to terrestrial growth)—* colorful berries—full sun means 6 hours—partial sun, 4 hours—diffused light, 2 hours indirect sun—semishade, light but no sun—small, to 12 inches—medium, 12 to 36 inches—large, 36 inches or more.

NAME	PLANT	FLOWER	LEAF	GROWTH	EXPOSURE
ACANTHOSTACHYS					
strobilacea	small	orange	reddish-brown	pendent	partial sun
AECHMEA					
*angustifolia	medium	yellow	greenish-brown	tubular	partial sun
calyculata	medium	yellow	green	vase	diffused light
caudata var. variegata	medium	orange	green, ivory	rosette	diffused light
chantinii	large	yellow, red	green, banded silver	vase	partial light
distichantha var. schlumbergeri	medium	blue	gray green	tubular	partial sun
fasciata	medium	blue	olive-green, silver banded	vase	diffused light
filicaulis	small	white	glossy green	vase	diffused light
*Foster's Favorite	large	blue	wine-red	vase	diffused light
*fulgens var. discolor	large	violet	olive-green, purple	vase	diffused light
*luddemanniana	large	red and lavender	green mottled dark green	vase	partial sun
*Maginali	medium	blue	olive-green, purple	vase	diffused light
*mertensii	small	red and yellow	green	tubular	diffused light
*mexicana	large	red and yellow	pale green	vase	partial sun
nudicaulis	medium	red and yellow	gray-green, silver banded	tubular	partial sun
orlandiana	medium	white and yellow	green, banded brown	vase	partial light
ornata	medium	pink	gray-green	vase	diffused light
*penduliflora	medium	blue	reddish brown	rosette	diffused light
pineliana var. minuta	small	yellow	gray, rose, red-brown	vase	partial sun
*pubescens	medium	ivory	gray-green	tubular	diffused light
racinae	small	red, yellow, black	green	vase	shade
ramosa	medium	yellow	apple-green	vase	diffused light
recurvata var. ortgiesii	small	pink	dark green	tubular	diffused light
weilbachii	medium	red, lavender	green	vase	diffused light
ANANAS					
†*bracteatus	large	lavender	green	rosette	full sun
†*comosus	large	purple	gray green	rosette	full sun
†*nanus	small	purple	dark green	rosette	full sun
ARAEOCOCCUS					
*flagellifolius	small	pink	reddish brown	bottle	partial sun
pectinatus	small	red	reddish brown	bottle	partial sun
BILLBERGIA					
amoena var. amoena	medium	green, blue	green	tubular	diffused light
amoena var. viridis	medium	green	green, red, cream, rose	tubular	diffused light

NAME	PLANT	FLOWER	LEAF	GROWTH	EXPOSURE
distachia	small	green, blue	pinkish brown	tubular	partial light
euphemiae	small	pink, blue	gray green	tubular	partial light
Fantasia	medium	blue	green spotted cream & pink	tubular	partial light
horrida	medium	green, blue	brown with silver bands	tubular	diffused light
leptopoda	small	green, blue	green, spotted cream color	tubular	diffused light
lietzei	small	cerise	green	tubular	diffused light
meyeri	medium	blue, green	gray green, silver banded	tubular	partial sun
nutans	medium	blue, green	dark green	pendent	diffused sun
porteana	medium	green	gray green	tubular	diffused light
pyramidalis var. concolor	medium	pink	golden green	tubular	diffused light
sanderiana	medium	green, blue	green	rosette	diffused light
venezuelana	large	purple	brown with silver bands	tubular	diffused light
zebrina	large	golden yellow	gray green, silver flecked	tubular	diffused light

BROMELIA

NAME	PLANT	FLOWER	LEAF	GROWTH	EXPOSURE
†*balansae	large	rose, white	dark green	rosette	full sun
†*humilis	medium	pink, white	green	rosette	full sun

CANISTRUM

NAME	PLANT	FLOWER	LEAF	GROWTH	EXPOSURE
fosterianum	medium	white	green, mottled brown	tubular	diffused light
lindeni var. lindeni	medium	white	apple green, dark green	vase	diffused light
lindeni var. roseum	medium	white	dark green	vase	diffused light
lindeni var. viride	medium	white	dark green	vase	diffused light

CATOPSIS

NAME	PLANT	FLOWER	LEAF	GROWTH	EXPOSURE
berteroniana	medium	white	apple green	bottle	diffused light
floribunda	small	white	apple green	bottle	diffused light
†morreniana	small	yellow-white	apple green	vase	diffused light
nutans	small	yellow	green	vase	diffused light

CRYPTANTHUS

NAME	PLANT	FLOWER	LEAF	GROWTH	EXPOSURE
†acaulis	small	white	green	rosette	diffused light or semishade
†beuckeri	small	white	greenish-cream	rosette	diffused light or semishade
†bivittatus	small	white	pinkish brown, silver green	rosette	diffused light or semishade
†bromelioides	small	white	greenish brown	rosette	diffused light or semishade
†bromelioides var. tricolor	small	white	green, pink, cream striped	rosette	diffused light or semishade

NAME	PLANT	FLOWER	LEAF	GROWTH	EXPOSURE
†fosterianus	medium	white	dark brown and crossbanded	rosette	diffused light or semishade
†zonatus	small	white	brownish green to copper, crossbanded	rosette	diffused light or semishade
DYCKIA					
†brevifolia	small	orange	dark green	rosette	partial sun
†fosteriana	medium	orange	silver green	rosette	partial sun
†frigida	large	orange	waxy green	rosette	partial sun
†leptostachya	medium	orange	reddish brown	rosette	partial sun
†rariflora	small	orange	silver gray	rosette	partial sun
GRAVISIA					
aquilega	large	orange, yellow	apple green	vase	partial sun
fosteriana	large	orange-yellow	green	vase	partial sun
GUZMANIA					
berteroniana	medium	yellow	wine-red or green	rosette	diffused light or semishade
lingulata	medium	orange-red, white	apple green	rosette	diffused light or semishade
lingulata minor	medium	orange	green	rosette	diffused light or semishade
lingulata Peacocki	small	orange-red, white	yellow-green	rosette	diffused light or semishade
Magnifica	medium	white	shiny green	rosette	diffused light or semishade
monostachia	medium	red, brown, white	dark green	rosette	diffused light or semishade
musaica	medium	golden white	green, dark green, red-brown	rosette	diffused light or semishade
vittata	medium	white	light green, chocolate banded	rosette	diffused light or semishade
zahni	medium	white	light green, penciled maroon-red	rosette	diffused light or semishade
HECHTIA					
†argentea	medium	orange	glossy green	rosette	full sun
†glomerata	medium	white	glossy green	rosette	full sun
†rosea	medium	pink	brown-red	rosette	full sun
†texensis	medium	pink	brownish green	rosette	full sun
HOHENBERGIA					
ridleyi	large	lavender	golden green	vase	full sun
stellata	large	purple	golden green	vase	full sun
NEOREGELIA					
ampullacea	small	white, blue	glossy green, brown cross-bands	rosette	partial sun

NAME	PLANT	FLOWER	LEAF	GROWTH	EXPOSURE
carolinae	medium	purple, white	dark green	rosette	diffused light or semishade
carolinae var. tricolor	medium	purple, white	green, white stripes	rosette	diffused light or semishade
cruenta	medium	blue	golden green	rosette	partial sun
johannis	small	lavender, blue	green	rosette	partial sun
Marmorata	medium	white	green, marbled with red	rosette	partial sun
spectabilis	medium	blue	olive green	rosette	partial sun
NIDULARIUM					
billbergioides	small	white	green	rosette	diffused light
var. citrinum	medium	white	green	rosette	diffused light
fulgens	medium	blue	yellow green, spotted dark green	rosette	diffused light
innocentii var. innocentii	medium	white	purple	rosette	diffused light
innocentii var. striatum	medium	white	green, striped ivory	rosette	diffused light
innocentii var. wittmackiana	medium	white	green	rosette	diffused light
procerum	large	orange, red	yellow green	rosette	diffused light
regelioides	medium	red	dark green	rosette	diffused light
ORTHOPHYTUM					
fosterianum	medium	white	apple green	branched rosette	diffused light
†navioides	small	white	green	rosette	diffused light
†saxicola	small	white	green	rosette	diffused light
†vagans	small	white	metallic green	rosette	diffused light
PITCAIRNIA					
†andreana	small	yellow, orange	gray green	branched	diffused light
†corallina	medium	red	gray green	stalk	diffused light
†paniculata	medium	red	green	stalk	diffused light
PORTEA					
kermesina	medium	pink	green	vase	diffused light
*petropolitana var. extensa	large	pink, green, lavender	apple green	rosette	diffused light
PUYA					
†alpestris	large	blue, green	green	dense rosette	full sun
†berteroniana	large	blue	green	dense rosette	full sun
†chilensis	large	green, yellow	green	dense rosette	full sun
QUESNELIA					
arvensis	large	blue and white	dark green, banded	rosette	diffused light or semishade
humilis	small	purple	gray green	tubular	diffused light

NAME	PLANT	FLOWER	LEAF	GROWTH	EXPOSURE
liboniana	medium	red, blue	dark green	tubular	diffused light
quesneliana	large	blue, white	green	rosette	diffused light
RONNBERGIA					
columbiana	small	purple, white	greenish brown	tubular	semishade
†morreniana	small	blue	bright green, spotted dark green	stalk	semishade
STREPTOCALYX					
longifolia	medium	white	dark green	rosette	diffused light
*poeppigii	large	pink	pinkish green	rosette	diffused light
TILLANDSIA					
anceps	small	blue	dull green	dense rosette	partial sun
brachycaulos	small	purple	reddish-brown, green	dense rosette	partial sun
bulbosa	small	purple, white	silver green	bottle	diffused sun
butzii	small	purple, yellow	green, spotted purple	bottle	partial sun
caput-medusae	small	blue	greenish	bottle	partial sun
cyanea	medium	violet blue	dark green	rosette	diffused light
fasciculata	medium	blue	gray green	rosette	diffused light
flexuosa	small	white	gray green, silver banded	bottle	partial sun
geminiflora	small	yellow, lavender	purplish gray	rosette	partial sun
ionantha	small	red, blue	silver green	rosette	partial sun
juncea	small	blue, purple	olive green	rosette	partial sun
lindenii	medium	royal blue	dark green	rosette	diffused light
paraensis	small	red, yellow	dull green	bottle	partial sun
punctulata	small	purple, white	gray green	rosette	partial sun
streptophylla	medium	lilac	silver green	bottle	diffused sun
tricolor	medium	violet, white	dark green	rosette	partial sun
VRIESEA					
barilletii	small	yellow	green	rosette	diffused light or semishade
carinata	small	red, yellow	green	rosette	diffused light or semishade
carinata Mariae	medium	yellow, green	green	rosette	diffused light or semishade
fenestralis	large	yellow	light green, lined dark green and purple	rosette	diffused light or semishade
heliconoides	large	white	dark green suffused with red	rosette	diffused light or semishade
hieroglyphica	medium	yellow	green zigzagged with purple	rosette	diffused light or semishade
imperialis	large	yellow	wine-red	rosette	diffused light or semishade

NAME	PLANT	FLOWER	LEAF	GROWTH	EXPOSURE
malzinei	small	yellow, green	claret color	rosette	diffused light or semishade
perfecta	medium	yellow	green	rosette	diffused light or semishade
petropolitana	small	yellow, orange	green	rosette	diffused light or semishade
schwackeana	medium	yellow	dark green, spotted purple	rosette	diffused light or semishade
splendens	small	yellow	green with purple bands	rosette	diffused light or semishade
WITTROCKIA amazonica	medium	white	dark green with purple	vase	diffused light
superba	medium	blue	dark green tipped red	vase	diffused light

EASY-TO-GROW BROMELIADS

Acanthostachys strobilacea
Aechmea angustifolia
Aechmea fasciata
Aechmea fulgens var. discolor
Aechmea mertensii
Aechmea ornata
Aechmea pineliana var. minuta
Aechmea racinae
Billbergia amoena var. amoena
Billbergia euphemiae
Billbergia horrida
Billbergia meyeri
Billbergia nutans
Billbergia venezuelana
Catopsis floribunda
Cryptanthus acaulis
Cryptanthus beuckeri
Cryptanthus bromelioides
Cryptanthus fosterianus
Cryptanthus zonatus
Guzmania lingulata
Guzmania vittata
Guzmania zahni
Hohenbergia stellata
Neoregelia carolinae
Neoregelia johannis
Nidularium regelioides
Orthophytum fosterianum
Pitcairnia corallina
Pitcairnia paniculata
Portea petropolitana var. extensa

Quesnelia humilis
Tillandsia butzii
Tillandsia geminiflora
Tillandsia ionantha
Vriesea barilletii
Vriesea carinata
Vriesea malzinei
Vriesea petropolitana
Vriesea schwackeana
Vriesea splendens

BROMELIADS FOR SUNNY LOCATIONS

Aechmea luddemanniana
Aechmea mexicana
Ananas bracteatus
Ananas comosus
Bromelia balansae
Bromelia humilis
Dyckia (most species)

Hechtia rosea
Hechtia texansis
Hohenbergia ridleyi
Hohenbergia stellata
Puya alpestris
Puya chilensis

BROMELIADS FOR PARTIAL SUN

Aechmea angustifolia
Aechmea mexicana
Aechmea nudicaulis
Billbergia distachia
Billbergia euphemiae
Billbergia Fantasia
Billbergia meyeri
Gravisia aquilega

Gravisia fosteriana
Neoreglia cruenta
Neoreglia johannis
Tillandsia anceps
Tillandsia brachycaulos
Tillandsia butzii
Tillandsia flexuosa
Tillandsia geminiflora

BROMELIADS FOR DIFFUSED LIGHT

Aechmea caudata variegata
Aechmea fasciata
Aechmea orlandiana
Aechmea ramosa
Aechmea weilbachii
Billbergia nutans
Billbergia porteana
Billbergia venezuelana
Billbergia zebrina
Cryptanthus (most species)
Neoregelia ampullacae

Neoregelia Marmorata
Orthophytum fosterianum
Orthophytum vagans
Portea kermesina
Portea petropolitana var.
   extensa
Quesnelia arvensis
Streptocalyx poeppigii
Tillandsia bulbosa
Tillandsia fasciculata
Tillandsia streptophylla

BROMELIADS FOR SHADE

Aechmea filicaulis
Cryptanthus beuckeri
Cryptanthus fosterianus
Cryptanthus zonatus
Guzmania lingulata
Guzmania Magnifica
Guzmania monostachia
Guzmania musaica
Guzmania zahni
Nidularium innocentii var.
   innocentii

Ronnbergia columbiana
Ronnbergia morreniana
Vriesea barilletii
Vriesea carinata
Vriesea fenestralis
Vriesea heliconiodes
Vriesea hieroglyphica
Vriesea petropolitana
Vriesea splendens

TYPES OF INFLORESCENCE

Star-shaped

Aechmea fasciata
Guzmania lingulata
Guzmania Magnifica
Hohenbergia ridleyi
Hohenbergia stellata
Nidularium billbergioides

Cone-shaped

Aechmea luddemanniana
Ananas bracteatus
Bromelia balansae
Guzmania monostachya
Guzmania zahni
Streptocalyx poepiggii
Vriesea malzinei

Branched

Aechmea caudata variegata
Aechmea chantinii
Aechmea fulgens discolor
Aechmea maginali
Aechmea pubescens
Aechmea ramosa
Billbergia saundersii
Catopsis floribunda
Catopsis morreniana
Dyckia leptostachya
Pitcairnia paniculata
Portea petropolitana var.
  extensa
Vriesea hieroglyphica

Pendent

Acanthostachys strobilacea
Aechmea racinae
Billbergia distachia
Billbergia euphemiae
Billbergia nutans
Billbergia venezuelana
Billbergia zebrina
Pitcairnia corallina

SOURCES OF PLANTS AND SUPPLIES

California Jungle Gardens
11977 San Vicente Blvd.
Los Angeles, Calif.

Bromeliad list

Fantastic Gardens
9550 South West 67th. Ave.
Miami, Fla.

Large selection of top-quality plants; list available.

Holmes Nurseries
P.O. Box 17157
Tampa, 12, Fla.

Good stock; brochure available.

Lee Moore
P.O. Box 504B
Kendall, Fla.

Bromeliad list (50 cents).

Juluis Roehrs
Rutherford, N.J.

Top-quality plants; catalog available.

Earl J. Small
P.O. Box 11207
St. Petersburg, Fla.

Catalog

Alberts & Merkel
Boynton Beach, Fla.

Excellent color catalog (25 cents); good selection of plants and hybrids.

INDEX

Boldface references are to illustrations